FICTION

PAGE 20

PAGE 26

FEATURES

BRAIN BOOSTERS

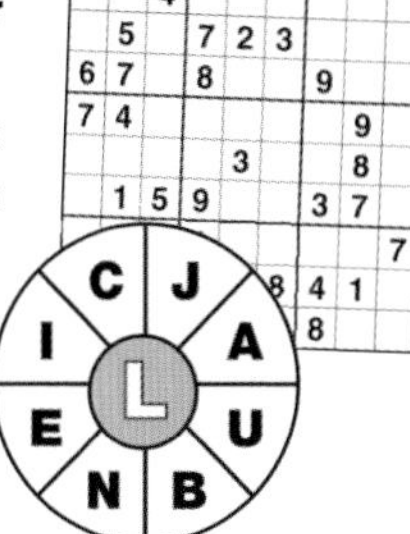

FANCY THAT!

TEATIME TREATS

COVER PICTURE: REX FEATURES

Smiles Around The World

Royal smiles have offered friendship throughout the world and made the UK the centre of global attention

Our Cowboy Princess!

Kate certainly has the knack of choosing the perfect outfit for every occasion – and it's rubbed off on her husband, too! For a trip to a rodeo during their royal tour of Canada, Kate and William donned jeans, cowboy shirts, boots – and ten gallon hats!

South Pacific – With A Royal Twist!

Not only does the Duchess of Cambridge know how to dress appropriately, she also knows all the actions. When presented with a grass skirt and floral crown to welcome her and the Duke to the Polynesian island of Tuvalu, Kate showed her appreciation by joining in the display of hula dancing!

All Smiles

A flash of Kate's perfect smile has melted hearts across the globe and, on this occasion, had Malaysian hearts all a-flutter. In fact, rumour has it that it was Kate's smile that first attracted William. Caring, fun-loving and natural – that smile says it all.

Just Hanging Around!

Anything William can do, daredevil Kate can do, too! She's never been one for standing on the sidelines while her action-man husband has all the fun. Exploring the mysterious rainforests of Malaysia is just one of the many things she's participated in, having fun during official tours.

More overleaf

Lady in Red

Kate chooses her official outfits with care – she knows what suits her slim figure and isn't afraid of being bold when it comes to colour. Bright red is a particular favourite with Kate, whose dark hair and pale skin provides the perfect contrast to this eye-catching colour.

The Look of Love

Described as a "second honeymoon", William and Kate's Royal Tour of the South Pacific certainly provided a glimpse of the true love and affection between the happy couple. In between their royal duties, the happy couple managed to sneak away for a couple of romantic nights in a tropical island hideaway.

Smiles All Round Down Under

When Queen Elizabeth and Prince Philip attended the final event on their 2011 tour of Australia, The Great Aussie Barbecue, 200,000 well-wishers turned up to bid a fond farewell to the monarch. "We will return to the United Kingdom with fond memories of our time here and the warm Australian welcome we received," said the Queen.

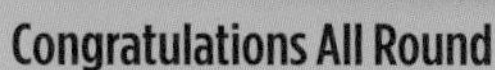

Congratulations All Round

To celebrate her Golden Jubilee in 2002, the Queen travelled around the world, including visits to Jamaica, New Zealand, Canada and 70 British cities and towns. Despite clocking up over 40,000 miles of air travel, the Queen kept on smiling for the massive crowds waiting to greet her everywhere she went.

More overleaf

The Royal Wave

The Queen was in Kenya when she heard of her father's death in 1952, so she must have had mixed feelings when she returned to Africa for the 1956 Royal Tour of Nigeria. Accompanied by Prince Philip (Charles and Anne were being looked after by their grandmother), the Queen's visit ended in Lagos, where thousands of masked warriors performed a spectacular dance.

All smiles in Barbados in 1989

Royal Babies

Queen Elizabeth

The Queen lived with her parents, the Duke and Duchess of York, at 145 Piccadilly. The family only moved to Buckingham Palace following Edward VIII's abdication.

Princess Margaret

Princess Margaret was born in a Scottish castle in the middle of a thunderstorm – a sign of the stormy times that lay ahead for the Queen's younger sister?

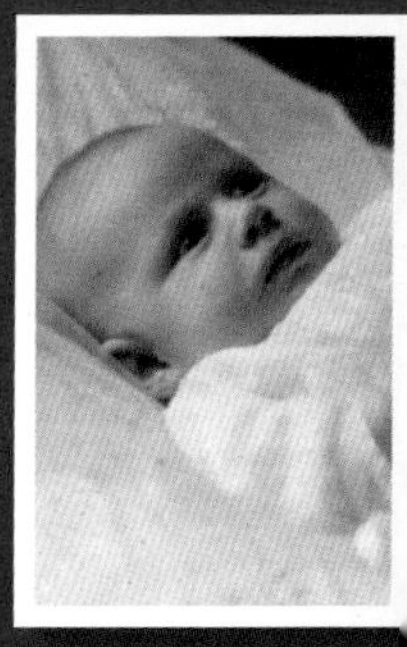

PICTURES: ALAMY, PRESS ASSOCIATION, REX FEATURES

Cheers!

A toast to their respective countries – and, perhaps, their friendship? Following Ronald and Nancy Reagan's visit to Windsor Castle in 1982, when the President went horse riding with the Queen, Queen Elizabeth and Prince Philip spent time at the Reagans' Californian ranch during their 1983 tour of America.

The Universal Language of Smiles

The Queen meets Indira Ghandi, Prime Minister of India and the world's first female prime minister, during her 1983 Royal Tour of India. This is one of almost 300 official overseas visits Queen Elizabeth has made during her 61-year reign.

Prince Charles

When Charles Philip Arthur George was born, the BBC very formally announced that Princess Elizabeth was "safely delivered of a prince". Unlike today's media frenzy!

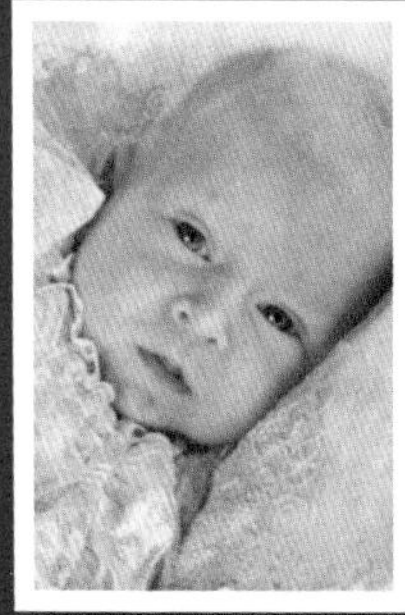

Prince William

The birth of Charles and Diana's first child saw thousands of people gather at Buckingham Palace to hear the official announcement of the birth of the new royal baby.

By best-selling novelist

Sue Moorcroft

Being Unfaithful to Jessica

Accidents can happen, but so can forgiveness – in fact you could say it was a crash course in romance…

There's something unusual about the van that trundles past me as I freewheel the long final swoop on my daily cycle ride home from work.

It's not that it overtakes me, giving me a flash of its owner's name on the side in red – Tom Patrick.

It's not that it's travelling in reverse away from Tom Patrick's house, where he's lived for the last few weeks. Tom with his shaggy fair hair and the incredible mouth, who's been sending me smiles ever since he moved in and even beginning conversations that feel suspiciously like chat-ups.

It's that Tom Patrick isn't driving the van. That's what's unusual. Nobody is.

A girl with multi-coloured hair is screaming along behind.

"No! Oh no!"

Tom Patrick's sprinting to catch her.

"Gemma, leave it, you'll get hurt!"

His dark brows are curled and his arms and legs beating like pistons.

The van gathers speed as it shimmies down the side of the postbox outside number eleven, smacks a rude kiss on the lamp post at number seventeen, then ricochets off into the drive of number twenty-six, tucked away at the bottom of the close, and buries itself in a pretty blue hatchback.

Its pursuers slither to a standstill. The screech of metal-on-metal ringing in my ears, my heart convulses as I skid to a halt beside them and let my bike topple to the ground.

"Jessica?" I whimper.

Tom Patrick's head whips around.

The van smacks a rude kiss on the lamp post then buries itself in a blue hatchback

"Who? Where?"

I manage to point a trembling finger at the mechanical carnage. "Jessica!"

Tom flings himself onto all fours to peer frantically beneath the vehicles.

"Where?"

Suddenly my voice is an outraged yelp.

"Jessie-Car, you idiot. My lovely, lovely car – the one with your van stuck in its side! You've wrecked my beautiful Jessie-Car."

Continued overleaf...

ILLUSTRATIONS: THINKSTOCK, MANDY MURRAY

Continued from previous page

He springs to his feet and turns on me, clutching his heart and wearing a thunderous scowl.

"The *car?* I thought Jessica was a person. I nearly called an ambulance."

I treat him to a thunderous scowl of my own.

"Sure you could manage the phone? It appears the simple operation of a handbrake's too difficult for you."

The girl with the peacock hair whispers, "I'm sorry. It's my fault." She bursts into tears.

"Now you've made my sister cry," snaps Tom.

"But, Jessica…" I stutter.

"Yes, well. Obviously I'll help you deal with the formalities," he mutters, testily.

In a frigid atmosphere I take pictures with my phone camera, trembling at the sight of the damage done to Jessica's formerly gorgeous curves.

Tom stomps about organising rescue trucks and we ignore each other except for me to spell my name for his insurance company, "C-a-r-o-n B-r-y-a-n," and a quick spat about my no claims bonus.

When our sorry vehicles are being hauled away, forlorn and undignified, their noses hooked up in the air, Tom finally has the grace to apologise, but then he spoils it by adding, "Lucky it's only a car and no-one was hurt."

I glare my best daggers.

"Only a car? I haunted garages to find that model in just that shade of blue, with grey upholstery and carpet – *and* a cup holder."

His eyes begin to dance.

"Wow. A cup holder. No wonder you're heartbroken, you'll never get another cup holder –"

"So I'm in love with my car. I'm glad that amuses you." Blinking back tears, I stalk indoors.

The next day, all I can think about at work is my empty driveway. No, it's not all I can think about – I think about how unlikely it is that Tom will send me any more flirtatious smiles or come up with reasons to talk to me. That makes me feel even worse than the state of poor Jessica.

Not long after I cycle home, I answer my door to a bouquet on legs. The pink carnations and white pom-pom chrysanthemums say in Tom Patrick's voice, "May I come in?"

"I suppose so." I stand back and the bouquet and the man shuffle in.

His shaggy hair falls over his eyes as he tries, awkwardly, to make things better

"I owe you an apology," Tom says, tentatively, laying the enormous floral arrangement on the kitchen table.

"That's true." But I feel myself beginning to melt. He does look apologetic. My heart shivers at the way his hair falls over his eyes as he tries, awkwardly, to make things better.

"You had every right to be upset when my van wrecked your car. It was just that…" He tries his heartbreaking smile and I have to think of my lips as

cardboard in order not to respond because, shivery heart or not, I don't want to let him off too lightly.

He sighs. "I was terrified that Gemma was going to be hurt, then when I thought someone called Jessica had been…"

"You took it out on me," I finish.

He winces. "Sorry. Gemma's my kid sister and I'd agreed to teach her to drive. I shouldn't have left her alone in the van. She began playing about with the controls – she took it out of gear and I suppose the handbrake couldn't have

Continued overleaf…

Continued from previous page

been on properly. Then she got out to see where I'd got to and the movement was enough to set the van in motion."

"So we really are lucky that she wasn't hurt," I concede. His eyes are a delicious shade of green, and his lips are just delicious.

He smiles. "Gemma's sorry, too. She wanted to come with me but she's only just stopped bawling. I didn't want her to start again."

I shift uncomfortably. Poor thing. She made a mistake. She didn't mean any harm.

I sigh. "Tell her that I'm getting over it – and Jessica will be mended in time."

His eyes light up. "Thank you! And at least your car's not beyond repair. My van's totalled, I'm afraid. I'll have to wait for the insurance company cheque before I can buy something else."

I know the finest and therefore busiest garage in town is working on Jessica, but it means quite a wait until my darling's restored to me in her former glory, and my bike's not much use on the supermarket run.

I miss Jessica. I miss the rubbery smell of her carpets and the smoothness of her steering wheel. I miss washing her on Sundays and admiring her paintwork winking in the sun, the thrum of her engine and even the squawk of her horn.

Still, I'm better off than Tom because at least Jessica's coming back to me in a few weeks. Tom's van went to the scrapyard.

I decide to forgive him.

In order to do so I shower, blow-dry my hair into a tousled-but-gorgeous mop, apply make-up then stroll up the hill to his red brick house.

He flings open his door. "Caron – the very person!"

I flush and give what I'm afraid might be a simper. "Really?"

"I've something to show you. You'll love it! Come into the garage."

He even slings a warm arm around me as he guides me to the side of the house. Tingles shudder down my spine.

He grasps the garage door and hoists it up, and it's…

"It's like Jessica but gold," I gasp.

"She certainly is," he agrees, proudly. "And newer. And sportier."

The car's gorgeous. Every molecule of its shining paint, every spoke of its alloy wheels, every inch of its black leather upholstery shouts, *Drive me! I'm fabulous!*

Tom strokes the gleaming bonnet.

"I decided to go upmarket. The van's been great but as I had to buy a new vehicle, I thought I'd go for something more..."

"Beautiful," I groan. I can't help adding, "Poor darling Jessica's still in bits and you'll be roaring past while I cycle around in the rain."

"Ah." He hesitates. "I guess your insurance doesn't pay for a courtesy car while Jessica's being repaired?"

I sigh. "Nope. Not rich enough for a policy like that." Then I pull myself together. It's not all Tom's fault; accidents happen. So I take a deep breath and paste on a sporting smile.

"Can I sit in her for a minute?"

"Of course." He sounds subdued.

He even lets me have the driver's seat. I stroke the dashboard and he shows me how the air-conditioning works. "And the CD player? And the windows?"

He grins crookedly and pushes a panel. "Here's the cup holder."

"For two cups," I say, wistfully. "I'm not usually unfaithful to Jessica but, oh, this car is so lovely..."

I tear myself away, eventually. My forgiving of Tom seems to have fallen flat, so I sigh goodbye and prepare to trudge back down the hill.

Tom stops me, frowning as if pain.

"Look," he manages. "You're right, it's not fair." He takes a deep, deep breath and croaks out, "If it's OK with Jessica you can use my new car until she gets back." He thrusts the ignition fob at me. "She's called Goldie. Just – just look after her as if she were Jessica. OK?"

I swallow my amazement, gazing at Goldie, gleaming and glowing in the overhead light. She's lovely, she's new and shiny, she's...

...not Jessica.

"We could share her," I suggest. "Until Jessica comes home. If I can use Goldie to haul shopping around, I'll be better off than I've been since the accident."

He grins crookedly and pushes a panel. "Here's the cup holder. For two cups"

He sweeps me up in a big hug, his face one beaming smile.

"That's very generous, in the circumstances!" And he kisses me – a light friendly kiss... a kiss that somehow becomes something much more than friendly.

It takes a minute before we can even pause and pull back to gaze at each other.

His arms tighten around me.

"What about... well, we could share her to the cinema tonight?"

"We could..." I muse, pretending to take time to consider.

"She does have a cup holder for two."

"Oh well," I say. "In that case, I'm sure Jessica will understand."

Turn the page for more from Sue...

All About Sue

First published in My Weekly, the award-winning romantic novelist gives us a tantalising peek into her latest book

Where and when did you first get published?

Truthfully? It was in My Weekly in 1996. I'd already sold a story to one of your sister magazines, but they didn't use it for a while so I made my professional debut in your pages.

I sold another 85 stories, a serial and various articles before I finally sold a novel.

What was your first novel?

It was called *Uphill All the Way,* took place in England and Malta and came out in 2005. When I got the call from my agent, "I have an offer for you," I believe my side of the conversation consisted of me saying, "You're joking!" in various shades of disbelief. It was one of those moments of utter euphoria that are a privilege to experience.

That evening, I insisted on going out for dinner because, I said, "Novelists don't cook." I've since discovered this to be untrue. I returned home that evening to a phone call from my new editor to congratulate me. Bliss.

Since then there have been another six novels, a "how to" book, four serials, monthly columns and – my first love – more short stories, and I've won awards. So look what you started!

After selling my first novel I went out for dinner, saying, "Novelists don't cook..."

What's your favourite novel?

A Town Like Alice by Nevil Shute which I first read when I was nine. Dad liked Nevil Shute and we'd watched the film – as an army family, war films were popular with us. *Alice* gripped my imagination as a war story and a love story, and began my lifelong love affair with Nevil Shute's books.

Where do you work?

In my study, mainly. It's a bit of a squeeze and never tidy but it contains a comfortable chair and the communications paraphernalia essential to home workers – computer and phone.

I work on trains and in hotel rooms or at conferences if appropriate, and sometimes people employ me to lead courses in Italy and other lovely places.

■ ***Is This Love?* is published by Choc Lit, November 2013, £7.99.**

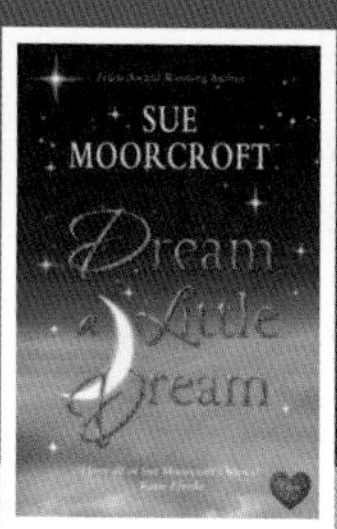

So what's your new book, *Is This Love?*, about?

It concerns different types of love. Love for her sister Lyddie keeps Tamara Rix living in Middledip village – but her boyfriend Max sees it as competition for what Tamara feels for him.

Lyddie has difficulties after a hit-and-run accident in her teens. The book opens when Jed Cassius, Lyddie's teenage sweetheart, returns to tell her family who was driving the car.

When Tamara meets Jed again it's with instant recognition and attraction – because she used to have a crush on him, too.

Sue is also a writing tutor and awards judge

We need to hear more about those delicious characters!

Tamara's fun. She's a yoga instructor and whizzes around gyms and village halls running classes. She goes after what she wants – as long as it doesn't mean abandoning Lyddie – loves spike-heeled boots and interesting hair.

Jed's fascinating. He has no qualifications, having spent some years living "outside the system", so how has he ended up with a great job managing the affairs of rich businessman Tom Hilton and living in a luxury apartment? He's recruited his stepbrother, Manny, to take care of Mr Hilton's security and then he arranges for Tamara to teach yoga to Mr Hilton's young wife, Emilia, too.

As for Lyddie… well, I think everyone will love Lyddie. Her behaviour's quirky but she has oceans of love to give to people, puppies, ponies and chickens. She forms a particular attachment to Emilia, which creates compelling dynamics between various characters – and huge headaches for Tamara and Jed, too.

PICTURES: THINKSTOCK

The Fairy in the Bathroom

The strangest things happen in the middle of the night when you just can't sleep…

By Paula Williams

nnie lay rigid in bed, her nerves stretched to breaking point at the sound of a bulldozer being driven at full throttle across a bumpy field.

Finally she could stand it no longer. She gave Kev, her husband, a sharp elbow in his well-covered ribs.

"Wh – whatsamatter?" he spluttered.

"You're snoring again. Honestly, it sounds more like a flipping –"

"Bulldozer. So you say. I'm sorry, love. I'll try not to…."

His voice trailed away as he drifted back to sleep, leaving Annie still wide awake and staring at a flap of peeling wallpaper in the far corner of the room.

She sighed, got out of bed and went to the bathroom. As she opened the door, the towel rail fell down. Again.

"Talk about useless," she muttered crossly to herself as she picked up the towels. "He promised to fix that ages ago. But no, he's got far more important things to spend his time on – like stretching out on the sofa watching the football." She propped the rail against the wall. "As for decorating our bedroom, if I had a pound for every time he promised to do something but never got round to it, I'd be that rich I'd never have to work again."

Annie had been married to Kev for nearly forty years and most of that time

His snoring was so bad, she wouldn't be surprised if the neighbours complained

PICTURES: THINKSTOCK ILLUSTRATIONS: MANDY MURRAY

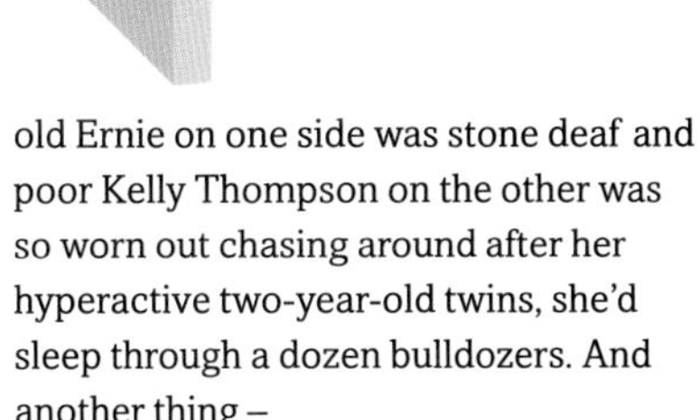

old Ernie on one side was stone deaf and poor Kelly Thompson on the other was so worn out chasing around after her hyperactive two-year-old twins, she'd sleep through a dozen bulldozers. And another thing –

The house was in need of a good makeover

they'd rubbed along together well enough. But lately, it seemed that everything he did (or, as was more often the case, didn't do) got on her nerves.

She put her scratchiness down to lack of sleep. His snoring had got so bad, they'd have had complaints from the neighbours if it wasn't for the fact that

Annie stopped, mid-grumble, at the sight of a spider in the bath. One of those huge black ones with long, foldaway legs and sharp yellow eyes.

That was another thing about Kev. He hated creepy-crawlies so there was no point getting him out of bed to come and deal with it.

She placed the long-handled back

Continued overleaf...

Continued from previous page

brush close enough to the spider so it could climb up it, which it did with such speed that Annie jumped back quickly and banged her elbow on the corner of the hand basin. Just because she wasn't afraid of spiders didn't mean she wanted one running up her bare arm.

"Congratulations! Your kindness has been noted and you are now entitled to an appropriate reward."

Annie whirled round, her heart thudding. Was there someone downstairs? She was about to call out for Kev when she realised, with a rush of relief, that it could only be the answering machine in the sitting room. It would be one of those annoying recorded messages telling her she'd won the holiday of a lifetime provided she was stupid enough to call this number and part with wodges of hard-earned cash.

Yet when she reached the phone, there was no message flashing. Now she thought about it, the voice had sounded weird – shrill like those tin whistles the children loved and used to drive her mad with when they were little.

"I'm over here. On the mantelpiece."

There it was again, but when she went across to the mantelpiece, there was nothing there – except for a piece of broccoli, the size of a pea. How on earth had that got there? She tutted and went to flick it into the grate.

"Oi! Watch out!"

She froze. "Who? What?…"

"It's who, if you don't mind," the small tinny voice said rather crossly. "I'm the Broccoli Fairy."

"Yes, of course you are," Annie said.

"Don't ask. Some substandard magic she bought on the internet went wrong"

"And I'm in the middle of a particularly silly dream, which serves me right for having that extra helping of chocolate pudding.

"Next thing, I suppose, I'll be careering around Marks & Spencer on a skateboard, wearing nothing but a feather boa. Broccoli Fairy, indeed."

"I suppose you think fairies should be called Cobweb, Primrose or some other equally silly girly name?

"Well, this is the twenty-first century, you know, and Fairydom has moved with the times, even if you haven't. What's so bad about broccoli anyway? Don't you know it's the new wonder food and if you humans ate more of it, you'd all be a lot healthier?"

Annie couldn't argue with that. She'd been telling her children the same thing for years.

"Anyway, I don't have time to stand here nattering," the Broccoli Fairy went on. "As if I haven't got enough to do, I've had to come charging down here in the middle of the night. But a debt's a debt and must be repaid."

"Now just hang on a moment," Annie protested. "I don't owe anyone anything."

"Not you. Me," the fairy said. "That spider you saved from the bath? That was Cauliflower, my sister."

"Your sister? But how –?"

"Don't ask. Some cut-price, substandard magic she bought off the internet went horribly wrong. But we'd rather not talk about it. Still, because of what you did for Cauliflower I've been empowered to grant you three wishes.

"Come on then," she went on with an impatient toss of her small coppery head. "What's it to be? How about a lifetime supply of broccoli, for starters?"

"I don't think so, thanks. Do you really mean I can have anything I want?"

"All you have to do is think of three things that are important to you and we will maximise them."

Annie looked around her. "Well, there's this place," she began, uncertainly. "It's a right tip, isn't it? The whole place needs a total makeover, like on the telly –"

The room was suddenly flooded with such an intensely bright light that Annie was blinded for a second.

When her vision cleared, she was standing in the middle of the most beautiful room she'd ever seen. It looked like something from one of those posh lifestyle magazines.

She pulled back the rich brocade curtain and looked out into the street. Everything was still the same – except that Kev's dirty old motorbike, which he'd always claimed he was going to do up one day, was no longer propped against the wall.

She went into the kitchen, then up to the bathroom. Her whole house had been redecorated and refurnished from top to bottom. It was, without doubt, the mother of all makeovers.

"Well? It is to your taste, isn't it? We know these things, you know."

"It certainly is." Annie gasped in delight. "And what about money? Does that mean I can have as much as I want? For ever?"

"You only have to say the word and it's yours – and the broccoli, too, if you like."

"Just the money," Annie said quickly. "No broccoli."

The fairy shrugged. "Your loss," she said. "And your third and final thing? Make sure it's something that really matters to you, won't you? Because it's your last chance and once it's done, it cannot be undone."

"I've thought," Annie declared. "I'm not going to be silly and squander it. I've got this touch of arthritis in my knee and the doctor says it's my age and I'll just have to learn to live with it. So I'm going to wish for good health. What

Continued overleaf...

Continued from previous page

could be more sensible than that?"

"Nothing, although you probably would find your health would improve dramatically anyway if you increased the amount of –"

"Broccoli in my diet." Annie completed the sentence for her. "Yes. And I will, I promise. But if I could just have my third wish please?"

"You've got it."

And she had. The pain in her knee had gone – and the one in her elbow, where she'd cracked it against the hand basin. She felt different all over, as if she'd lost a few pounds and gained a few inches in height.

"Health, wealth and a lovely home. What more could I want?" she cried, "Just wait until I tell Kev."

It felt as though she was dancing on air as she skipped up the thickly carpeted stairs with a speed and agility she hadn't possessed for years.

"Kev," she called out excitedly as she burst into the bedroom. "You'll never guess what's happened. Wake up, quick, and see all this –"

She looked around, bewildered. The room was decorated in soft, peachy tones, the furniture was sleek pale wood and a shimmering satin quilt covered the king-size bed.

But the bed itself was empty.

"Where's Kev?" she asked.

"Kev?" The Broccoli Fairy was on the pillow where Kev's bald head should have been but wasn't. "Who or what is Kev?"

"My husband, of course. Where is he?"

"You didn't mention a husband when you listed the three most important things in your life," the fairy observed. "So he can't really mean that much to you, can he?"

"Of course he does." Annie's eyes filled with tears. "None of this – the house, the wealth, even the health – matters if I haven't got Kev."

"Then you should have thought about that sooner and put him top of your list. Sorry. I've got to go now. Things to do. Bye."

"No, please. Wait! Can't you undo one? Say, the house thing? After all, if I'm as rich as you say I am, I can easily buy another house."

The fairy folded her arms and shook her russet head. "Can't be done. I did warn you – once it's done, it cannot be undone."

"But there must be a way –"

The Broccoli Fairy shook her head. "If I live to be two thousand and ninety eight, which I probably will, I'll never understand you humans. According to your file, this is the Kev you're always complaining about. The Kev who keeps

"If I live to be two thousand and ninety-eight I'll never understand humans"

you awake with his snoring, falls asleep in front of the telly and never does any decorating."

"That's true, but he brings me a cup of tea in bed every morning… and always lets me put my cold feet on his warm ones."

Her tiny visitor harrumphed. "But with the looks and money I've given you, you could easily get another, better Kev."

"You don't get it, do you?" Annie cried. "I don't want another Kev. I want *my* Kev. None of this counts for anything if I don't have him to share it with."

"Sorry. Rules are –"

"I wish I'd never saved your wretched sister. Next time I see a spider in the bath, I'll turn the taps full on and flush it away."

"You wouldn't do such a dreadful thing! She can't swim!"

"Try me," Annie retorted fiercely.

"OK. You win," the Broccoli Fairy said sulkily. "I'll pull some strings and reverse the wishes – but you do realise it's all or nothing, don't you?"

Annie gulped, said a silent, sad farewell to her beautiful house and nodded.

"I just want my Kev back," she whispered brokenly.

"Fair enough. And to show that I do have a soft side, I will leave you something as a thank you for saving my unfortunate sister."

"That's very kind of you. I'm –"

Annie got no further. There was another blinding flash. When she opened her eyes, the bedroom was back to its normal, shabby state, the slight pain was back in her knees and Kev was back in their saggy old bed, which rocked gently to the blessed sound of idling bulldozers.

What was it the fairy had left? Annie wondered sleepily. *That lovely flat screen telly, maybe? Or the deep pile carpet? Should I go and check it out?*

Of course not. It was just another of those silly dreams she kept having, wasn't it? She got into bed, snuggled up to Kev and wrapped her cold feet around his warm ones.

Meanwhile in the bathroom, a large black spider picked her way across the hundreds of broccoli heads that filled the bath, toilet and hand basin and spilled on to the floor. At last she found what she was looking for.

She settled down in the middle of the single creamy white cauliflower, folded away her foldaway legs, closed her sharp yellow eyes and smiled contentedly.

THE AUTHOR SAYS…

"I used to try all sorts of things to get my sons to eat broccoli when they were little and the Broccoli Fairy was one of them. And no, they still don't like broccoli!"

Goldie And The Three Hoods

She got hopelessly lost in the woods but in doing so, she found her way to a brand new life and an exciting future

By Teresa Ashby

oldie stopped in a clearing and spun round. She'd lost the path some time yesterday afternoon just before it got dark and none of this looked familiar. One tree looked very much like another, and she could be feet from a pathway and not even be able to see it.

She'd hoped to hear traffic on the road that ran through the forest, but all she heard was the distant hum of a plane overhead, birds yakking in the trees and small furry things rustling in the leaves.

She could see the headlines now…

WOMAN SURVIVES SIX MONTHS IN FOREST BY EATING WORMS AND LICKING DEW FROM LEAVES!

Ugh, she was hungry, but she wasn't about to start eating worms… yet.

She'd spent a wakeful night curled up at the foot of a tree, constantly brushing bugs away, hoping that first light would make things clearer. But she was as hopelessly lost as ever, so she'd decided to just keep moving.

She'd only come into the forest for a quick run away from prying eyes. When she'd asked people to sponsor her for the coming charity marathon, they'd laughed, but the one thing she was really good at was running and she was determined to show them.

When she first realised she was lost, panic set in and she'd run through the trees, screaming for help. Fat lot of good that did. Of course, she'd left her mobile phone in the car, in case she lost it.

Hysterical laughter bubbled up and burst out, and as she laughed and gasped, she inhaled a smell.

Her laughter stopped abruptly. "Bacon," she said. She sniffed the air. It was still and misty, but there it was – the unmistakable mouthwatering smell of breakfast. She cupped her hands round her mouth and yelled, "Hello!"

Her voice echoed through the trees, startling birds and other creatures. For a moment, the sky above turned black with birds as they rose in a cloud, but within seconds all was quiet again.

The smell got stronger as she hurried onwards and soon she could see smoke curling up, mingling with the morning

Goldie wondered if they had missed her at work yesterday. Probably not

PICTURES: THINKSTOCK ILLUSTRATIONS: MANDY DIXON

Which way to turn?

mist, but smoke all the same.

"A house," she cried as a tiny cabin came into view. She broke into a run and, reaching the house, banged on the door. Someone must be in, but no one answered. In desperation she went inside.

"Hello," she called. "Anyone home?"

The door opened into a living room with a small kitchen area at one end. A wooden table stood in the centre with a coffee pot in the middle and three plates, each piled high with bacon sandwiches.

She grabbed a mug, poured herself a coffee and sipped the hot liquid. "Oh, bliss," she whispered. "I so needed that."

She wondered if they had missed her at work yesterday. Did anyone wonder why she hadn't come back after lunch? Probably not. They all thought she was scatty and brainless. Well they'd be right, wouldn't they? Big fat tears rolled down

Continued overleaf...

Continued from previous page

her face. She was so tired and hungry and fed up. Goldie the klutz, they called her. Gullible, not very bright and the butt of so many jokes, her confidence was at an all-time low.

Mr Jessop, her boss, had heard the teasing, but he'd turned a blind eye and when she'd approached him about promotion, he'd only laughed at her. "You've no substance, Goldie," he'd said.

She rubbed away a tear. Right now, her growling stomach was her biggest problem. The sandwiches looked so delicious, and she hadn't eaten since breakfast yesterday. She'd skipped lunch to have her run and she'd promised herself a good meal when she got home, but of course, she never made it.

"I'm sorry," she said as she sat down in one of the chairs. "I'll pay you back, whoever you are, but I'm famished."

She picked up a sandwich and bit into it. "Ugh! Mayonnaise! Who puts mayonnaise in a bacon sarnie?"

She moved to the next seat and checked under the top slice of bread. The bacon was doused in ketchup. That was more like it. She smiled and took a bite.

"Yuk!" A fried egg was hiding under the ketchup. It was worse than the mayo.

One plate remained. She checked under the top slice. No mayo, no egg. It looked perfect. She took a bite and her stomach murmured its appreciation.

The sandwiches were so delicious, she cleared the plate. Whoever had made them would be back soon. She would explain what had happened and they'd help her find her car so she could pay them back. She moved to one of the comfortable-looking old armchairs.

The first one wasn't as comfy as it looked. No matter how she sat, springs prodded into her flesh. The second one was so squishy, she felt as if she was being swallowed. The third snuggled her up, warm and soft. She almost fell asleep as all the trudging through the forest and being awake most of the night began to catch up with her. As she kicked off her trainers, she noticed a staircase.

Surely no one would mind if she had a little nap. She pushed down on the arms of the chair as she rose and there was an ominous crack. Leaping up and spinning round, she watched in disbelief as the chair disintegrated.

LOST WOMAN STEALS FOOD AND VANDALISES HOME!

True the chair was old and shabby, but it had been so comfortable – and now somehow she'd destroyed it. But she would explain. She'd buy these good people a chair to replace that one.

But first she had to sleep… then she realised that something was hidden in the shattered upholstery. She pulled out a small cloth bag. It was full of jewellery. A wooden box was stuffed with money. *Oh, how sweet,* she thought. *The little family keep all their valuables hidden in a chair.*

The narrow staircase led up to a single bedroom which had three beds. It smelled of the damp boots and empty bottles littered around the floor, but she dropped onto the first bed with relief – and sprang right back up again.

It was like lying on concrete – and no

The shotgun propped up at the foot of the bed made her rather nervous…

wonder, for more treasure was hidden in the mattress. She tried the second bed, but she hadn't been there for a minute before the feather pillows made her sneeze. Besides, the shotgun propped up at the foot of the bed made her nervous.

BIZARRE DEATH OF WOMAN WHO SHOT HERSELF IN HER SLEEP!

"Third time lucky," she said to herself as she flopped onto the last bed. She smiled as she buried her head in a soft foam pillow and pulled the warm duvet over her. As sleep overwhelmed her, she thought about her running and how she was going to abandon it. After all, it was stupid to entertain thoughts of being anything other than the office dogsbody. She was so unhappy at work. They all laughed at her behind her back – and sometimes to her face. Her name didn't help. It was her dad's fault. He'd had such a crush on Private Benjamin.

"Hey, what's this?" A voice woke her. "Someone's taken a bite out of my bacon butty."

It was a man and he sounded furious.

"Mine too!"

"You think you've got problems," another guy said. "They've eaten all of mine. We've been robbed! And look, my chair's smashed to bits."

"It's disgusting, it is! A man can't even go out to nick some milk for his coffee without being robbed."

There was clattering as they rummaged about downstairs.

"Nothing seems to be missing."

"Yeah, but what sort of person breaks into a place, smashes the place up, eats their breakfast and… trainers!"

Goldie sat bolt upright, clutching the duvet to her chin.

"They're girl's running shoes."

"How do you know they're for girls?"

"They're pink, stupid!"

She just knew they were all looking up at the ceiling. She could feel their eyes boring through the boards. She shook with terror. The headlines were becoming more and more vivid…

MISSING OFFICE WORKER FOUND BURIED IN WOODLAND – KILLED FOR STEALING A SANDWICH!

There was whispering and laughter, then they started up the stairs. Goldie shot out of bed and ran to the tiny window.

MURDERED GOLDIE FOUGHT HARD FOR HER LIFE!

"Oh, shut up with the headlines already!" she muttered. She flung the window open and began to wriggle through as the footsteps got closer. Before she dropped to the ground, she saw a stubbly face snarling at her from the doorway.

She landed on a carpet of pine needles, which softened her fall then she broke into a run, bare feet protesting. It hurt to breathe and the sandwiches felt heavy in her stomach, but the sound of the men coming out of the cabin behind her spurred her on.

Continued overleaf…

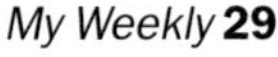

Continued from previous page

This time she was on a winding path and it led to a clearing where a black car was parked. She jumped in. No keys. The men were getting closer every second, shouting in fury. She fumbled with the sun visor and the key fell into her lap.

Sobbing now, she plunged the key in the ignition, rammed the car into gear and stamped hard on the gas. The car fishtailed, throwing up dirt and leaves and she saw the men in the mirror, covering their faces as grit blinded them.

The track through the forest was just about wide enough for the car and she kept her speed up, bouncing wildly over the uneven ground until at last she could see the road ahead.

A different headline flashed through her mind now…

RUNAWAY WOULD-BE MURDER VICTIM CRASHES GETAWAY CAR!

The car bounced from the lane onto the road and she'd no sooner put her foot down again than she heard sirens.

Crying with relief, she pulled over.

"Do you realise what speed you were doing?" the female officer asked.

"I was running away," Goldie cried and she blurted out her story. "I think they might be robbers," she concluded, her chest heaving as she tried to catch her breath. "There was a lot of money and jewellery – and a gun!"

There was no sarcastic, "You think?" as Goldie would have expected from work colleagues. Instead, the male officer put his hand on her arm.

"Are you alright?" he said. "That was a very brave thing you did."

"Brave?" she echoed. "Me?"

"It sounds like the Dobson gang. We've been after them for months."

When Goldie went into work the next day, everyone stared at her. She waited for the mean comments to start, but one by one everyone stood up behind their desks and began to clap.

Someone held a newspaper up. She really had hit the headlines.

BRAVE GOLDIE FOILS ROBBERS – DANGEROUS GANG ARRESTED.

"We're so proud of you, Goldie," Mr Jessop said. "We've invited the press here to interview you. It will be good publicity for the company."

"What a shame you'll have to cancel," Goldie said, feeling confident for the first time in her life as she handed over a white envelope. "My notice with immediate effect. As I'm so useless, you won't miss me if I leave straight away."

Jaws dropped as she turned on her heel and walked out. She had never felt this good about herself in her life.

It was the female police officer who had given her the idea.

"You should train to be a professional adventure instructor," she'd said. "You're obviously very fit."

A new life had called on her – and she was answering!

THE AUTHOR SAYS…

"I love fairy tales and it's fun to give them a new twist. I had little sympathy for the original Goldilocks, but I confess that I rather like Goldie!"

Brain BOOSTERS

Codebreaker

Each letter of the alphabet has been replaced by a number. We've started it off – see if you can fill the grid!

19	16	9	17	11	16	■	11	12 O	17 T	26 A	17	16
■	24	■	11	■	5	■	16	■	7	■	26	■
1	25	24	26	17	25	12	9	■	26	3	18	16
■	13	■	5	■	17	■	26	■	9	■	21	■
13	17	10	16	■	2	12	18	12	20	11	26	23
■	16	■	15	■	16	■	■	■	■	■	17	■
25	9	17	16	9	17	■	23	16	23	12	25	11
■	17	■	■	■	■	■	26	■	26	■	22	■
14	25	13	19	12	22	16	11	■	8	16	16	11
■	26	■	18	■	25	■	4	■	16	■	9	■
26	18	13	12	■	13	4	6	26	13	2	16	14
■	18	■	6	■	12	■	25	■	17	■	13	■
12	10	13	17	16	11	■	13	18	10	16	13	17

~~A~~ B C D E F G H I J K L M N ~~O~~ P Q R S ~~T~~ U V W X Y Z

1	2	3	4	5	6	7	8	9	10	11	12	13
											O	
14	**15**	**16**	**17**	**18**	**19**	**20**	**21**	**22**	**23**	**24**	**25**	**26**
			T									A

Solutions On Page 165

Tin Tan Tommy!

Thoughts of our daughter's future, and a name from the past, led us back hand-in-hand to a long-forgotten summer

By Angela Pickering

"And this is Ben," Amy said, her eyes sparkling with delight. "Ben Dobson."

The hand that I had thrust forward paused in mid air. "Dobson?" I mumbled.

"Pleased to meet you," said Ben, speaking for the first time.

I forced a polite chuckle. "Of course," I managed, and shook his hand. "You too."

We moved into the lounge where I had spread the coffee table with cake and teacups. "Tea? Or a cold drink maybe?"

"Ben's family come from Little Stormton," said Amy, "like you and Dad."

"Yes, you did mention that," I replied, handing them each a glass of fizzy drink. "Though you didn't tell me his surname."

"Did you know my dad, then?"

"Hello," interrupted Pete, my husband, bounding in like a puppy. "Great to meet you. Amy's told us so much about you."

I winced and, with a mother's instinct, felt Amy do the same. I caught Pete's eye, and shook my head the tiniest bit. The last thing you do is tell your daughter's new boyfriend that she's been talking about him.

"Keep it cool, Mum," Amy had already warned me. She'd obviously not bothered to warn her dad.

"Cake! Lovely," said Pete, ignoring the chilly vibes from his daughter. "Mum's been baking especially for you, Ben."

Goodness, could it get any worse? Oh yes, he could pull out the family album to show Ben snaps of Amy in her nappies.

I cut Pete a huge piece of cake. "Here," I said, "get stuck into that."

"We'll head upstairs now, Mum," said Amy. Pete spluttered into his tea

"We'll take ours upstairs, now, if that's all right, Mum," said Amy after a rather stilted attempt at small talk. "We're going to play some music."

Pete spluttered into his tea, and I coughed to cover it.

"Not too loud," I said, laying my hand on Pete's leg and squeezing it gently.

"Upstairs?" he squeaked once they'd gone. "Is he *allowed* in her bedroom?"

"I said they could," I told him.

PICTURES: ALAMY, THINKSTOCK ILLUSTRATIONS: MANDY DIXON

"As long as they keep the door open."

"Oh dear," he replied, shaking his head. "I'm never going to get used to this."

"Course you will, love," I said, offering him more cake. "Times change."

"Not with my daughter, they don't," he said, tilting his head and listening for any noise from upstairs.

"Stop it," I said. "You have to trust her."

"Hmmm. It's not *her* I don't trust."

"He's a Dobson, from Little Stormton," I told him.

Pete frowned. "That name rings a bell."

"Dobson's farms? Remember?"

Pete's eyes grew bigger and I could see him slipping back into our shared past. I took his hand and went with him.

Continued overleaf...

Continued from previous page

The heat was intense, bringing the scent of the corn up into our noses. I was clinging to his hand, Pete, my best friend from the village. Holding hands with boys was a new experience for me, and since Pete's was all hot and sticky, I wasn't sure I was too keen on it.

"There he is!" Pete shouted. "Tin Tan Tommy, I see Robert."

Robert popped up out of the corn and made his way over to us. He stood at my other hand, and I wondered whether I was supposed to hold his hand as well. It might be sticky too.

"Tin Tan Tommy, I see Shirley," cried Pete, as her red, curly hair floated above the golden stalks.

There were six or seven other village children dotted about in the cornfield. The game was to move about, popping up every now and then until spotted. The last to be seen was the winner. We weren't supposed to play in the corn, but then there were a lot of things we weren't supposed to do.

A shriek rang through the field. "Quick, run! Old Man Dobson."

A sudden sprouting of multi-coloured bodies flew from the corn, and a whole bunch of dusty legs pounded from the field.

"Split up," Robert yelled and we ran, helter-skelter, as the Land Rover came into view over the horizon. "He's coming."

The farmer. Old Man Dobson, we called him; terrifying creature of nightmares, rushing towards us on his green monster steed. Maybe the danger of it all was half the fun, but I for one didn't feel that way.

We ran, spiralling off into different directions, like firework sparks in a night sky. Fear made my legs pump faster than they ever had before. What would he do if he caught us? No one wanted to find out.

My hand slipped from Pete's and he ran on, oblivious. I sobbed and stood still, waiting for the awful vehicle to catch up. We were out of the corn by this time and there was nowhere to hide.

The Land Rover bounced across the mud towards me. I hitched a breath. My mum would be so upset when she found out I'd been eaten by the monster.

The Land Rover stopped in front of me. The door swung open and a pair of brown trouser legs appeared. He was enormous, scowling and obviously keen to deal with a little girl who'd flattened some of his precious corn. I was trembling so much I could hardly stand.

A grubby hand snatched at my fingers. "Molly – move." I was almost deafened by Pete's shout.

Somehow Pete dragged me along, into the alleyway behind our houses.

"He can't follow us in here," he gasped.

I blinked through tears of fright and exhaustion. "You came back," I sniffed.

"'Course I did – you're my girlfriend, aren't you?"

He was eight, I was six. I was his girlfriend.

A huge voice roared from the end of the alley. "You kids, keep out of my fields.

I'll tell your parents. You see if I don't."

"You see if I don't," repeated Pete, clutching my hand as we sat together on our sofa and returned to the present. Our little girl was upstairs with one of them. A Dobson.

I gazed up at him and sighed. "We weren't allowed out for ages after that," I said. "But you're still my hero, Peter."

"Still my girlfriend," he replied, then started to laugh. "Poor Old Man Dobson. We must have driven him crazy."

I agreed. "The damage we must have done to his crops."

"He never did catch us."

"I don't think he ever really meant to," said Pete. "What could he have done? If he'd laid a finger on us, my dad would have had him for breakfast."

"Your dad was bigger than my dad," I confirmed, smiling at our old saying. "I don't know if he was bigger than Old Man Dobson, though."

I managed to laugh a little, then, as we reminisced. We'd gone our separate ways as we grew up, but somehow we drifted back together. The cornfields had all gone by the time we got married; new houses had taken their place.

"Good times," said Pete with a sigh.

"Oh yes, mostly," I replied, but I didn't remind him of my occasional nightmares when the corn was high, and a green Land Rover endlessly chased a little girl.

Amy and Ben came back into the room. "We're off for a walk now, Mum," Amy said.

"I think we knew your grandfather," Pete said to Ben. "Dobson Farms?"

Ben smiled. "Nah, nothing to do with my family." Ben shrugged. "We're Johnsons, not Dobsons."

I blushed. What a stupid mistake.

Ben was still talking. "My dad remembers the farm, though. He used to play in the fields around here."

"Really?"

"Yes," said Ben. "Sounds like fun."

"Oh, it was." Pete beamed. "Not for the farmer, though."

"Old Man Dobson," I whispered.

"Yeah, that's it," agreed Ben. "You guys must have known my dad."

Pete frowned. "What's his name, then?"

"Bob – Bob Johnson."

So, a few months later when the two families finally met up, I knew Pete wouldn't be able to resist it.

"Tin Tan Tommy," he cried jubilantly. "I see Robert."

And I held my hand out to take Robert's at last. It wasn't sticky at all.

Pete couldn't resist. "Tin Tan Tommy," he cried out jubilantly. "I see Robert..."

THE AUTHOR SAYS...

"I was dreaming of my childhood the other night – when we used to play in the corn. That poor farmer; he was a scary man, though. He never caught us."

Biker Days

An adventurous grandad, a headstrong grandchild and an unconventional vicar… a recipe for disaster?

By Jill Davis

o I need you to take Grandad to church today. Use my car…" George's mum sneezed, reinforcing why she was unable to carry out her usual Sunday morning duty, and buried her head beneath the rumpled bedcovers.

"OK. What time will I pick him up?"

The feeble answer caused George to abandon any thoughts of an exhilarating burn-up on the Bonneville. Unless… "Mum, do you suppose Grandad might like to go on the back of the bike?"

The answer was a snuffly snore. George grinned. Grandad had always loved motorbikes; it wouldn't hurt to give him the choice.

Grandad's usual flat cap was replaced by a midnight blue helmet and, with him seated on the pillion, George gunned the bike and opened up the throttle, experiencing a thrilling adrenaline rush as the engine's low growl changed into a throaty roar.

Picking up speed, George felt Grandad's grip tighten suddenly and experienced a stab of guilt, wondering if this had been such a good idea. Easing off the throttle, the ride became more sedate than burn-up, but at least they'd arrive safely.

At the church, George's brief elation dissipated at the thought of being confined for the next hour with a crusty old vicar and his dutiful followers. There was a small crowd of elderly folk chatting as George helped Grandad off the bike and took the helmet, watching as he pulled the checked flat cap out of his pocket and pulled it on at a rakish angle.

Three of the waiting men hurried over.

"Good on yer, Harry," chuckled one, as he stood admiring the bike.

"A Bonneville!" exclaimed another. "You lucky old fella."

"Are you trying to kill him?" barked the third man, glaring at George. "Have you young men no sense? Taking a man his age on that death trap." Now he berated Grandad. "You silly old fool. You're not the ton-up kid any more, Harry."

"Ah, Fred. You never did like us bikers, even back when we were lads."

The other two men murmured their agreement.

"Young George here's a chip off the old block," said Grandad, "although I wouldn't have minded if she'd gone a little bit faster."

The low growl changed to a throaty roar as George opened up the throttle

Continued overleaf…

PICTURES: THINKSTOCK ILLUSTRATIONS: JIM DEWAR

George loved to travel at speed

Continued from previous page

George removed her helmet, enjoying the look of shock on Fred's face as he realised his mistake.

Harry grinned mischievously. "Meet my granddaughter Georgina, named after her grandmother – you remember her, don't you? And her love of bikes? Young George here was practically raised on them. It's a family joke that she has engine oil flowing through her veins. Good memories, eh Fred?"

Fred gave a strangled cough of indignation as he turned away and pushed past the others, who were sniggering like wrinkled teenagers.

"Priceless," chortled one.

George turned to Grandad, trying not to laugh at the look of satisfaction on his face. "Gramps, you're wicked."

Harry smiled broadly, his face glowing with exhilaration. "I know, but that ride reminded me of the day your grandmother took me out on her bike. That was the moment I fell for her. You know the story; Fred had already asked her out and she'd accepted, but after our ride she told him she couldn't go, and then invited me out. Fred never forgave either of us."

His voice softened. "I miss her, but you've got her spirit alright."

"Thanks, Gramps." George squeezed his arm gently.

The vicar was standing waiting at the doorway. "Hello, Harry. Everything alright?" he asked.

"Never better," he said. "My granddaughter brought me today. Vic, meet George."

"Ah," the vicar replied, smiling at George. "I wasn't expecting that."

George hadn't expected a vicar to look like that, either. Not in the least bit crusty. Or old.

"I did see you on a Bonneville, didn't I?" The vicar's face lit up. "It's my absolute favourite."

"Really?" George gasped.

"Yes, really. I might be a vicar but I'm a secret biker at heart. Sometimes it's good to surprise people, don't you think?"

He grinned and strode down the aisle, cassock swishing around his legs to reveal a flash of denim jeans underneath.

"See," Grandad whispered. "Church isn't so bad after all, is it?"

George shook her head in wonder. Who knew what other surprises this Sunday morning would bring?

He smiled at her. "Sometimes it's good to surprise people, don't you think?"

THE AUTHOR SAYS...

"I read an article about a newly assigned young vicar, who had long hair, wore a leather jacket and rode a motorbike. There had been a mixed reaction from parishioners."

Fancy That!

Pink facts that make you go "**Wow!**"

◆ **The pink colour of a flamingo is caused by carotenoid pigments in their diet of shrimp, plankton and crustaceans.**

◆ Flamingos are monogamous and only lay a single egg each year.

◆ **While flying in a flock flamingos can reach 35mph.**

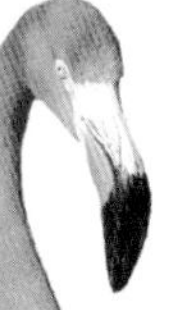

The word flamingo comes from Spanish meaning fire and refers to their bright pink colour

Pink salmon is the most abundant salmon species in the North Pacific

◆ **The singer Pink's real name is Alecia Moore – Pink was a school nickname.**

◆ In the USA there is a cheap version of mince or ground beef called "pink slime"!

◆ **In the USA, female office workers are "pink collar".**

The antioxidant lycopene gives pink grapefruit its colour

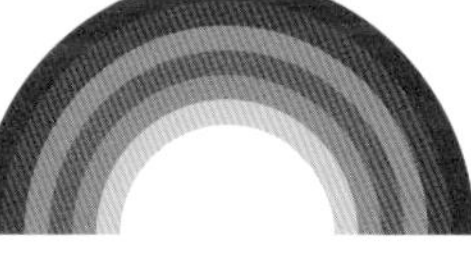

◆ Madder roots were used to produce all shades of the colour pink.

◆ **The colour pink is believed to have a tranquilising effect on the mind.**

◆ In America a pink slip refers to an informal notice of termination of employment.

Pink ribbon symbolises breast cancer awareness

WORDS: BABS BEATON PICTURES: THINKSTOCK, ISTOCKPHOTO, REX FEATURES

My Best Pub Buddy

This chap sounded just like Jen's lonely, stubborn old dad – so she decided to take matters into her own hands…

By Stella Whitelaw

The personal columns of the local newspaper don't usually interest me as I am not into single dating, selling or buying unwanted items and I spotted the advertisement by sheer chance.

There it was in bold print. It immediately caught my eye.

Wanted
Pub Buddy
At the Rose & Crown
Three nights a week
All expenses paid
(Topics: fishing, military history, current affairs)

I liked the way topics of conversation got top billing. He sounded like a lonely widower fed up with sitting on his own with his pint, surrounded by mini-clad, gel-haired youngsters. Maybe the expenses would cover a few drinks, crisps and a taxi home?

There was one person who fitted this bill exactly. My dad. He was mad on fishing, spending hours on the end of the pier, in any weather. He'd survived years in the Royal Marines and was stir-crazy about politics. None of these subjects interested me for more than thirty seconds, but I forgave him when he brought home a sea bass for our supper.

And Dad was another lonely widower, only he wouldn't admit it. Every evening he sat glued to the telly, hardly watching anything unless it was about fishing, military history or current affairs.

"It's all rubbish these days," he'd complain nightly. "And this lager is tepid and flat."

"Sorry, Dad. I'll get you another one."

"Don't bother. I'm off to bed. No point in staying up. Goodnight, Jen."

No point in staying up? It was only half past nine. I curled up on the sofa with a pad and pen. I was going to answer that ad. How I'd get my dad there, to the Rose & Crown, was a different problem. Still, I'd put that one on hold for another day.

So I wrote as if I was my dad. A few well-chosen words about the biggest fish

"I'm off fishing," announced Dad the next evening. This was my opportunity

PICTURES: ALAMY, THINKSTOCK ILLUSTRATIONS: MANDY DIXON

caught, the sandiest, dustiest war, the worst political cock-up.

Not a word about my mum because I missed her too much to write about her. Perhaps I would, one day.

I'm off fishing," announced Dad, the next evening. It was pouring. He was wrapped in yellow oilskins, had his rod, his pail and his revolting bait and a flask of

Continued overleaf...

Continued from previous page

coffee. This was my opportunity.

"See you at the Rose & Crown at nine?"

He looked at me suspiciously. "Why?"

"You'll be frozen. You'll need a stiff brandy. I'll buy you a double."

He thought about it.

"All right, Jen. Rose & Crown. About nine. I might be late if I've got a bite."

I had the letter all ready to hand in to the manager of the Rose & Crown. I also wanted to suss out the Pub Buddy and make sure he wasn't a weirdo. I didn't want my dad drinking with a weirdo – even with all expenses paid.

It was still pouring at a quarter to nine so I put on my storm raincoat, Wellington boots and wrapped my hair up in a scarf. I was not out to impress, only to keep dry.

The pavements were glistening with rain and the gutters awash with debris. Typical British summer.

The Rose & Crown was busy. It was a popular pub, and a rinse of warmth and humanity engulfed the door as I opened it. Now, I am not a pub person. I am more a book and music person. But when I elbowed a space at the bar, I ordered a standard glass of house Merlot.

"Haven't seen you before," observed the grey-haired young man who served me. He worked at lightning speed. Complex orders were being thrown at him from each end of the bar, and he worked the till like a robot.

"I don't normally come into pubs," I said, pulling off my scarf as I sipped the Merlot. It was a good one – none of that cheap stuff that was only a sniff off vinegar. "I've come to hand in a letter to the manager."

"I am the manager," he said, spinning round to the till and punching in numbers. "Tony Burrows."

"It's in answer to that newspaper advert for a Pub Buddy."

"You're answering the advert?" Tony Burrows slowed down a fraction. His eyes narrowed. "Hardly your scene, lady. What do you know about fishing and military history?"

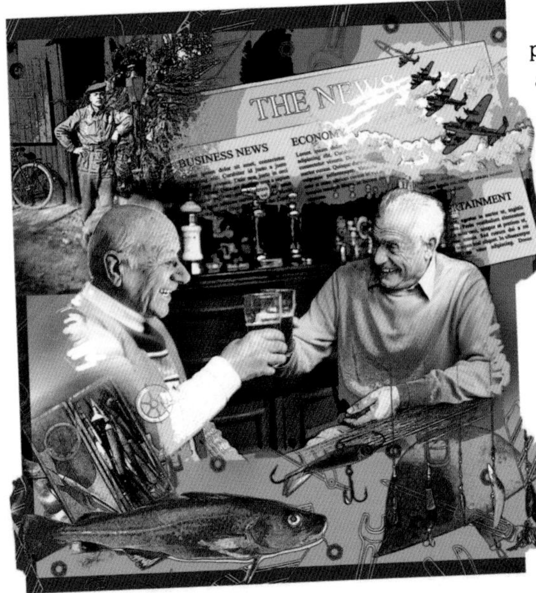

"Quite a lot actually, but not from personal experience. My dad is answering this advertisement. He'll be along later. Yellow oilskins."

The young manager was drawing pints by the legion. He knew exactly how to time the head. It was fascinating to watch him work.

"The Pub Buddy is there in the corner, by the fire. His regular place. A glass of Guinness on the table in front of him. Doing the crossword."

I looked over to the fireplace. A grey-haired man, wearing gold-rimmed glasses, was huddled over a newspaper, pen poised above the crossword, but the pen never moved. He wasn't filling in any of the clues. He sat like a statue as if he was pinned to the paper.

"He looks all right, but a bit lonely."

"He is alright. He's my dad."

"And he advertised…?"

"He's a very proud old man and he is desperate for a drinking companion." The manager was stacking glasses into the dishwasher as he spoke. He never stopped working.

"And I've answered the advertisement, on behalf of my dad. He doesn't know that I have. Not yet. He's another old man who won't admit to being lonely."

Just then the door opened and my dad struggled in, followed by a wet gust and a flurry of rain. He was soaked, rain dripping off his face. I went to help him out of his oilskins; there was a place in the porch where I could hang them to drip.

"What a night. Nearly got blown off the pier. I caught our supper, Jen, a couple of mackerel, but I need that brandy first."

"Sure," I said innocently. "It's such an awful night, the pub is packed. Would you mind sharing a table with that gentleman over there by the fire?"

"Do I have to?" he grumbled.

"Mention fishing, military history or current affairs and I think you will find yourself very welcome."

Two hours later, and my dad and the manager's dad were deep in conversation and arguments. They were enjoying the arguments. The table was littered with glasses and two empty chip baskets.

"I need to go home," I said, finishing my second glass of Merlot. "I still have marking to do for tomorrow."

"I'll make sure your dad gets home in a taxi," said Tony Burrows. He was beginning to look tired now. "All expenses paid, remember?"

"Mention military history and I think you'll find yourself very welcome"

"How do you know?" I asked, but I already guessed the answer.

He grinned. "I put that ad in the paper. My dad doesn't know about it either. He doesn't need to know, does he, Jen? It's just between you and me, isn't it?"

"Dad caught a lovely pair of mackerel this evening," I said. "I can put them in the freezer. Perhaps, one day, when you have an evening off, you might like to come round for supper?"

The manager of the Rose & Crown grinned. He nodded vigorously at me as he stacked glasses on an overhead shelf. "That's a date, Jen. Hang on, I'll order a taxi for you, too. You can't walk home in this weather."

The pub buddies were deep in conversation. They were putting the world to rights. But I thought the world was quite perfect at this very moment.

Say It With Flowers

Who knows what wonderful ideas will take root in a lively two-year-old's mind? Enjoy this heartwarming story

By Jan Snook

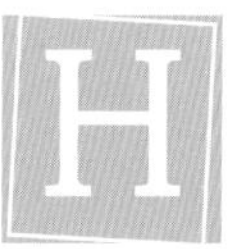er grandson peered interestedly at the food on the lunch tray as Moira moved the letter she had been writing out of the way, and smiled her thanks at the nurse.

"I don't like all *that* things," Jamie said, pulling a face and pointing at the salad.

Her daughter-in-law, Emma, looked at Moira over two-year-old Jamie's head and raised her eyebrows.

"Oh, but salad's delicious, Jamie," Moira answered. "Everyone likes salad."

"Be careful of my leg, sweetheart. Sit on this side and I'll tell you a story..."

Her daughter-in-law gave an approving nod. "You don't look very comfortable, Mum – do you need to sit up more? Can I give you a hand?"

"You most certainly can not," Moira said firmly, looking at Emma's large bump. "I'm fine. One of the nurses will help me in a while, don't you worry."

Moira supposed she ought to make an effort to eat her lunch, but she really wasn't hungry. She was used to being up and about – walking the dog, delivering meals-on-wheels, gardening – not stuck in a hospital bed, being waited on. No wonder she didn't feel like food; she wasn't using any energy at all. She picked up her fork, but Jamie opened his mouth to speak. He was still glaring at the salad.

"*I* don't like it," he repeated obstinately, "but my wabbit like it."

"A rabbit?" Moira said, putting her fork down again and looking at the excited little face. "Oh Jamie, when I come out of hospital you'll be able to show me. How exciting to have a pet!"

Jamie looked suitably gratified, and Emma stood up. "Will you be alright with him for a mo, Mum? I'm afraid I must find a loo. Joys of pregnancy and all that... You'll be okay?"

"Of course." Moira watched slightly apprehensively as Jamie scrambled up on to her bed. "Now be very careful of my leg, sweetheart. Come and sit on this side, and I'll tell you a story."

He looked up at her, a beatific smile on

Continued overleaf...

PICTURES: THINKSTOCK ILLUSTRATIONS: MANDY DIXON

Continued from previous page

his little round face. Oh dear, why had she said that? Moira could feel every story she'd ever known whooshing out of her head as he snuggled up expectantly.

"Well," she began, frantically racking her brains. She took a deep breath. "Well, Jamie, when I was a little girl, about as big as you are now, I lived with my Mummy and Daddy in a very hot country a long way away. It was in South America, which is so far away that I didn't see my Granny very often. We only came home to England once every three years. That's a very long time indeed."

It sounded absolutely barbaric, she thought to herself, like something from the dark ages. Yet it had only been the Fifties, and had been regarded as quite normal at the time. How dreadful it must have been for her grandparents. Even sending home a photo had taken weeks... How she would hate to have so little contact with Jamie! Not to mention the new grandchild, who was expected this very month.

"Well, when we did come back to England, I was very excited. I was going to see my granny! And my granny was very excited. She was excited for weeks and weeks before we arrived. And do you know what she did? She dug a special new flower-bed, and she sprinkled some flower seeds in a special way."

Moira smiled at the memory. Her grandmother had been a big fan of pink and white alyssum. It had been exactly right for her purpose, its neat clumps forming very clear lettering.

"She sprinkled the seeds so that they spelled out words. They said, 'Welcome home, Moira.' My Granny knew they would be ready exactly when we came home to England. Wasn't it a nice idea?"

Jamie was wriggling, and she looked down at him. He looked puzzled, and she could see his concentration wavering. "I'll show you what it looked like," she said, reaching for her writing pad and pen. On a clean sheet she began to draw a daisy-chain of letters.

"But," she said dramatically, as Jamie screwed up his face to look critically at her efforts, "what do you think happened?"

Jamie's eyes grew round.

"My granny lived next to a farm, and the very day before we arrived home, some naughty sheep got into her garden, and they ate most of the flowers."

"Draw the sheep!" Jamie said excitedly. "Draw the sheep, Granny!"

Moira obediently drew some more-or-less recognisable sheep, daisies hanging from their impudent mouths, and followed them with a picture of an angry woman (not remotely like her gentle grandmother), shaking her fist.

"Goodness, you look as if you're having a good time," Emma said, arriving back at that moment. "But I think Granny's probably tired now, Jamie, so we'd better go home. A nurse is on her way, Mum. We'll come again tomorrow."

Emma bent awkwardly to kiss her, and added, "You have thought about what I said yesterday, I hope? We really won't take no for an answer, you know."

"It's so sweet of you both," Moira said again, "but really, you'll be so busy, what with the new baby due and everything. You don't need me staying as well."

Emma squeezed Moira's hand.

"It would be great to have you, and think how useful if the baby decides to arrive in the night..."

"But to have your mother-in-law to stay... are you quite sure, Emma?"

"You're the nearest thing to a mother I've got," Emma returned stoutly, "so you're coming."

Moira watched as mother and son walked down the ward, hand in hand. She was sorely tempted – and she was getting better at walking every day, Moira conceded to herself. Maybe she really could be a help.

At last the day arrived when Moira was allowed to leave the hospital. Her son turned up to collect her and fussed over her as he settled her comfortably into the car.

"Are you quite sure this is okay?" Moira asked him tentatively, yet again. "With Emma, and the baby due and everything? I do worry that it's all too much for her, you know."

He leaned across and patted her knee. "I know you do, Mum. But honestly, it's fine. It really is. You're very welcome." He smiled to himself as he said it. "And there's no time to change your mind anyway," he pointed out. "We're here."

Emma and Jamie were at the door, the little boy jumping up and down, threatening to knock Moira over in his excitement.

"Come and see, come and see!" he was shouting, before she was even over the threshold.

He smiled. "There's no time to change your mind now, anyway – we're here"

"Oh yes!" Moira replied, beaming. "I want to see your rabbit!"

"Not my wabbit," Jamie said, looking perplexed. "Come and see!"

Moira followed him slowly into the kitchen, bemused.

"It was the fastest-growing thing we could think of," Emma said, smiling, "and the rabbit's been kept well away!"

Jamie was still hopping from foot to foot as Moira gazed at the enormous seed tray on the work surface. Tears pricked her eyes. The wobbly words were spelled out in cress and read, "*WELCOME HOME GRANNY*"

THE AUTHOR SAYS...

"I recently offered to tell a story to my grandson (before I'd thought of one) and suddenly remembered this true story of my grandmother's floral message and the hungry sheep..."

Ever The Optimist

With money at crisis point, the last thing Annette needs is her redundant husband having a creative renaissance...

By Ginny Swart

Hi, love. You're late back." Liam gave Annette a hug.

"It's Friday – I had to shop on the way home."

Something you could have done during the day if only you'd thought of it, she thought but didn't add.

Annette unpacked the groceries, which these days were just the absolute necessities. Their budget didn't allow for any treats.

She looked around the kitchen in exasperation. The breakfast things were exactly where she'd left them, and the rubbish bin was still overflowing.

"Oh Liam, you could have cleaned up!" she snapped. "What on earth were you doing all day?"

"Sorry, I got carried away and forgot the time." Liam looked embarrassed. "I had this great idea for a rockery, so I dug over that bit near the tool shed and carried those rocks from behind the garage. Susie, you're going to love it! I put a lovely little china castle on top, and I used those shells you collected last week. It looks like a mountain from fairyland."

Four-year-old Sue gave a squeal and rushed out to take a look.

Honestly, thought Annette wearily, unloading the washing machine, *I almost think Liam enjoys being out of work.*

In the four months since he'd been made redundant, Liam had never been busier – or, it seemed, happier.

He'd had to give up the smart company car and his weekly game of golf but he didn't seem to miss them at all. He'd kept busy by re-designing the front garden. He'd written a comedy for the local Dramatic Society and had started composing songs. Annette often came home from work and found him plunking away on his old guitar.

Sue loved this new, always-available daddy, and when he'd surprised her with a family of animal puppets he'd made himself, she demanded a puppet show every night. While she made the supper, Annette listened to the latest adventure, punctuated by Sue's giggles.

Sue loved this new, always-available daddy and demanded a puppet show

Continued overleaf...

PICTURES: THINKSTOCK ILLUSTRATIONS: MANDY DIXON

At the end he threw jelly beans to the audience

Continued from previous page

Since his retrenchment Liam's become much closer to Sue, she thought, *it's lovely for them both. But he has to find a job soon. Our bank balance is frightening.*

That evening, Annette had just finished the ironing when the phone rang and Liam answered it.

"Speaking."

She stood still and listened intently. Could it be a reply to one of the many job applications he'd made in the first weeks of being at home?

He came back looking cheerful.

"That was Sue's teacher," he explained. "Apparently Sue was telling her about my glove puppets and she asked if I'd come and do a show for the children at their Christmas party."

"Oh Liam, that would be lovely! I hope you said yes."

"Of course! I'll use the Wolf and do Little Red Riding Hood," he said. "I could add some songs, so the children can sing along. Do you think you could make me a small red cloak with a hood?"

Annette had always helped with dressing the puppets and she happily rummaged in her scrap bag for red material.

What a pity Liam hadn't chosen acting or singing as a career when he was younger, she thought, *he would have enjoyed it so much more than being an engineer.* But at 45 it was difficult to imagine him in a new career.

The puppet show was a huge success. When Little Red Riding Hood appeared, bobbing up and down across the little stage, the children let out a roar of recognition. A high squeaky voice said, "Ooh, goodness me – I didn't see you there, children!"

Liam was on top form, doing the different voices as he brought the characters to life. The class was riveted until the end when Little Red Riding Hood and her grandmother waved goodbye and tossed handfuls of jellybeans to the audience.

"Bye-bye Daddy!" shouted Sue. "That was my daddy! He made up those songs!"

The mother next to Annette smiled.

Liam was on top form as he brought the characters to life with different voices

"Was that your husband? He's very good. Is he professional?"

"Heavens, no," said Annette. "He's actually an engineer. Puppets are just a hobby of his."

"Thank you so much, Mr Howard," said Miss Morrison at the tea break. "That was lovely. I hope I can persuade you to do it again at our Easter party."

"I'd be happy to." Liam beamed.

"But Liam's sure to be working full-time by then, Miss Morrison," put in Annette firmly.

"Oh, yes... right..." muttered Liam apologetically.

Walking home, the weeks of anxiety got the better of Annette.

"That's just the problem!" she snapped. "You'd be quite happy doing puppet shows forever! You've got to find a proper job. How much longer do you think we can manage? Do you realise I've cut our housekeeping to the bone? That we haven't even hired a DVD in months? That – that I can't even buy a bar of chocolate any more? Why? Because we can't afford it!" She was close to tears.

"My name's with every employment agency in town," said Liam quietly. "It's not my fault there's nothing available."

"The shopping mall? What on earth do they need with an engineer?"

"I'm the maintenance man."

"A janitor!" He eyes filled with tears. "But you're a qualified engineer!"

"They need someone to fix things and I need a job. At least it's paid work." He took her in his arms and kissed her forehead. "Don't be so upset. It's not forever and we'll have something coming in every week. A nice little wage packet with my name on it."

"It will keep the bank manager happier, I suppose," she said dubiously. "But you won't be earning the sort of money you did before. You'll have to keep looking for a – a proper job."

"This is a proper job. I'll be the best janitor they've ever had at the Mall and I'll be climbing the corporate ladder before you know it."

How could he joke like that? Annette hugged him tightly. "It won't be for long," she whispered. "By Easter, you're sure to have found something better."

"This is a proper job. I'll be the best janitor they've ever had," he told her

Annette was tired of being the only one who worried about the practical things. Nevertheless, she felt wretched about her outburst and tried to make it up, but things were cool between them for a few days.

Then Liam greeted her one evening with a half-smile and a small slab of her favourite dark chocolate.

"What's this for?" she asked.

"To celebrate. I'm employed," he said.

"Liam, that's wonderful! Where?"

"The Jubilee Mall."

The first Friday after he started, Liam made a joke of his wage packet, bringing it home and emptying the cash onto the kitchen table.

"Here's my wages, do I get a coupla bob to go down the pub, then?"

"Don't be so silly," she grinned, but scooped up the money anyway. "I'll be able to pay the phone and the gas bill with this. Thanks, love."

Just in time, she thought. *Another day and the phone would have been cut off.*

Continued overleaf...

Continued from previous page

"It turns out that my boss is actually a fan of mine," he added.

"Oh?"

"Janet Dorset, the Mall manager. She was at the puppet show and recognised me when I went up to fix a window catch in her office."

"She must have a good memory."

"And good ideas. She asked if I'd do a puppet show for the kids at the Mall on Saturday morning."

"That's fantastic! I hope she'll pay you a bit extra for it."

Six months ago Annette would never have said that, but these days she thought constantly of ways to save money. *Well, someone has to think about it,* she seethed resentfully.

"I must work out a story – maybe make some new puppets." Liam's thoughts were leaping ahead. "And put together a music CD, something to introduce the show…" He went off to his work-room and she was asleep long before he came to bed that evening.

the letter that had arrived that morning, addressed to Liam Murphy, B. Eng. This had to be a reply to one of his applications. Maybe a job offer.

She couldn't wait for him to get home and open it.

"It's from Anderson's, over in Merton. They're offering me a post…" Liam skimmed through the letter, a delighted smile on his face. Annette felt an overwhelming relief. At last. A proper job!

"Uh-oh. It includes Saturday work. Mm, I don't know Annette. I don't want to work Saturdays. It doesn't sound ideal."

She couldn't believe her ears.

"What? This is the first job offer you've had in six months and you're thinking of turning it *down*?"

"Janet's asked me to do a regular entertainment morning at the Mall on Saturdays. She's offered a nice fee and I've written a whole lot of Easter stories for the puppets. Actually I was hoping you'd help me with the costumes for some rabbits and chickens…"

They lay side-by-side in bed, unable to sleep but not talking to each other

"Your husband is really talented." Janet Dorset had run into Annette at the supermarket, where she was looking in the bargain bin. "Everyone loved his puppets. The children so enjoyed that sing-along he did at the end. He's got a real knack with little ones, hasn't he?"

"Yes," said Annette shortly. "He has."

For all her enthusiasm, Janet hadn't yet offered to pay Liam for his Saturday show, and Annette wondered if she'd include it in his wage packet the following week. Wage packet. She still couldn't get used to the idea. Annette's mind was on

She was speechless and for a minute, Liam took her silence as agreement.

"I'm glad you understand, sweetheart. We'll be fine."

Annette exploded.

"Liam, you simply cannot choose to do puppets and stay as a janitor instead of taking this offer! You're being ridiculous. Have you seen the bank statement this month?"

"Doesn't it count that I've found something I really enjoy doing at last?" he asked quietly. "Money's all you ever think about these days."

"Well, somebody in this family has to!"

He growled and walked out, slamming the front door as he went.

Why should I feel guilty for being practical? fumed Annette. *It's time Liam recognised his responsibilities.*

In bed that night, they lay side-by-side, unable to sleep but not talking to each other.

Annette's thoughts were whirling. If she was honest, she had to admit that when he'd been an engineer Liam had often come home in a bad mood, sitting grumpily in front of the TV and mulling over problems he'd have to deal with the following day. But as a janitor he came home relaxed, full of ideas for writing or composing songs and eager to play with Sue. She had to admit they were a much happier family. She was due for promotion soon – they'd manage somehow. She turned to Liam and put her arms around him, smiling in the dark.

"How about a compromise?" she whispered. "Stay on at the Mall and do all the Easter shows but get out there take on bookings for more puppet shows for birthday parties over the weekends. And of course I'll make the Easter bunny costumes. I'm sorry, I've been a pig."

"No. You were right before, love, I ought to accept the Anderson job. The money's too good to refuse."

"Liam… it's taken me a while to realise this, but you were right. Money's not everything in life. We'll be alright, you'll see."

"Really?" He cuddled her, and she could tell he was grinning in delight. "Well, I could have business cards printed and hand them out to the mothers. Janet's already asked if I'd be interested in doing a special show over the Easter holidays, and have the puppets give out hand-made eggs from that ritzy chocolate shop."

"Wow! Their chocolate is the best!"

"Not only that but I've also been writing short pieces about life at the Mall; the odd things I see and hear. You'd be amazed what I pick up. I was thinking of approaching the local paper and offering to do a weekly human-interest column."

"That's a brilliant idea. You're so good at writing – maybe you'll become a regular journalist. Then some national editor will spot your column and ask you to write for them…"

"I haven't even submitted anything yet." He chuckled. "You're such an optimist, Annette."

"It could happen – anything's possible. Hey, just one condition…"

"What's that?"

"You make sure Susie and I each catch an egg at your Easter show!"

THE AUTHOR SAYS...

"So many people I know lost their jobs over the past few years, and it was only being optimistic that got them through. I think a wife who can understand her husband's dream helps a lot!"

Well Hello, Mr Dimples

After his first visit to my shop, I couldn't stop thinking about the handsome stranger in bike leathers…

By Christine Sutton

orry I took so long, Miss," said the elderly lady, handing me a Congratulations on the Birth of your Baby card. "My granddaughter has just had her first baby after seven years of IVF, so it had to be the right one."

"How lovely," I smiled, ringing up the sale. I hear all sorts of tales – mostly happy, but sometimes sad – and consider it a compliment that people share such stories with me.

It was now past closing time, so I followed the customer to the door intending to lock up after her.

He slid off his crash-helmet to reveal a smiling face and a shock of blond hair

Before I could do so a faceless figure loomed into view. I sighed with relief as he slid off his crash-helmet to reveal a smiling face with a smattering of freckles, topped by a shock of gold-blond hair.

"I know you're just shutting but can I please buy a quick card?" the man implored. "I've just had a call from my sister's husband saying she's in hospital, suspected appendicitis. Can't go to visit her without a Get Well card, can I?"

I stood aside to let him in and his smile broadened, putting cute dimples in his cheeks.

"Thanks."

He stepped past me with a squeak of leather. Mouse impressions aside he was very attractive and I followed his progress up the aisle. Then he glanced back and caught me looking and I felt myself go pink.

Snatching up a card he read the message, chuckled, and returned it to the rack.

"It's lucky Colin caught me," he said conversationally, selecting another. "A few minutes more and I'd have been on my way to France, just me, the bike and the open road."

"Sounds wonderful," I said enviously. "Will you still go?"

"Depends how she gets on. They're running tests right now to decide what to do next. This one's fine," he said, bringing it to the counter.

PICTURES: ALAMY, THINKSTOCK ILLUSTRATIONS: JIM DEWAR

Anticipating cartoon characters and a rude rhyme, I was surprised to see calming countryside and tasteful verse. "I'd have gone for humour," he said, as if reading my thoughts, "but Kathy's not into bedpans and saucy doctors. Thanks for staying open, I appreciate it."

"Have a good trip when you go," I said, closing the till. "Send me a postcard."

It was just a throwaway quip but he paused in the doorway. "Bit like shipping snow to Eskimos, but OK, I will." With a

Continued overleaf...

Continued from previous page

jaunty salute he closed the shop door and was gone.

It must have been the thought of my impending "milestone" birthday but I spent that night sitting at home wallowing in self-pity.

Here I was, almost thirty, and still no man in my life. An image of dimples and leather-clad legs kept popping into my head and I batted it away.

No point thinking along those lines, girl, I told myself firmly. *Mr Biker will soon be sitting astride his motorbike heading for the Channel Tunnel.*

The mouthwatering image did nothing to help my equilibrium and I crawled into bed feeling frumpy and forlorn.

My first customers next morning were a silver-haired gent and a small girl who stood perusing the birthday cards.

"Would Nanny like this one, do you think, Amy?" the old man asked, pointing to one with a sleek red sports car on the front.

"Don't be silly, Grandad," scoffed the girl, "that's a boy's card. This one's perfect for Nanny because she has a cat just like that."

"And not, sadly, a Lotus Elan," chuckled the grandfather.

We exchanged smiles over the young child's head.

They eventually bought the card with the cat on the front and left, leaving me feeling all warm and fuzzy inside.

I was still smiling when the bell tinkled again and I looked up to see Mr Biker coming in.

He was wearing a dove-grey leather jacket, black T-shirt and faded blue jeans, a lethal combination in the armoury of male clothing in my book.

"Now that's what I call a welcome," he said with a grin.

"Hmm?" I asked, distracted.

"The megawatt smile?"

"Ah, sorry," I said, "leftover from my previous customer. So sweet."

"I'm crushed," he said mournfully.

"Course you are," I laughed. "How's your sister?"

He shook his head. "Not brilliant, I'm afraid. They've ruled out appendicitis but as to what it actually is, no-one seems to know."

"So your trip's on hold presumably?"

"Until I know Kathy's OK, yes."

"France will still be there," I consoled him. "So what brings you back here? Another card?"

He frowned, as if the question had stumped him. "Er... yes, that's it, another card. It's Kathy and Col's third anniversary on Saturday. Is there a special card for that?"

"Well, the third anniversary is leather," I told him with a smirk, "so wrap yourself in a giant envelope and Bob's your unc!"

He wrinkled his nose. "Can't see them

being too impressed with that. Better stick to ribbons and bells."

Thinking I'd be more than impressed, I watched him select a card and then return to the till. I rang up the sale, spinning it out for as long as I could. Finally, there was nothing more I could do to detain him.

"Give your sister my best," I said, as he turned to leave. "I hope all goes well."

"Thanks," he answered. "I'll be seeing her this afternoon, so I'll do that. My name's Mike, by the way..."

"Sue," I told him in return. "See you."

The day dragged by, yet when six o'clock came I found myself reluctant to leave, thinking maybe Mike would drop by with news.

Sure enough, at three minutes past the hour he appeared. But instead of coming to the counter, I was horrified to see him head for the Condolences cards. A chill ran through me. Surely not?

"Oh, Mike, she didn't...?" I started, unable to contain my fears.

He looked up, then down at the card in his hand. "Oh, no," he hastily assured me, "Kathy's fine. Or as fine as she can be under the circumstances. Sadly, it was an ectopic pregnancy. She'll be OK and should still be able to have children, but right now..."

I nodded sadly. "How awful for her. She doesn't know me, of course, but, please, tell her I'm thinking of her."

Spotting a pink envelope protruding from his pocket, I gasped in mock-shock. "Is that another shop's card I see? Not been unfaithful to us, have you?"

He looked sheepish. "Afraid so. I was expecting you to have gone by now, so was going to slip it under the door. But since you're here..." He pushed it across the counter at me.

"You know about my birthday tomorrow! But how?"

He bit his lip. "Umm, actually, it's just a thank you note for staying behind yesterday. But it's great that tomorrow's your birthday, gives me another excuse to come back."

Excuse?

"I'll be here first thing for a card. Maybe I could take you for a birthday drink, too?"

He'd paused by the gift-wrap and I imagined waking tomorrow and peeling off layers of paper to find him inside. It was a thought so distracting it took me a moment to realise he was still speaking.

"Is that another shop's card I see? Not been unfaithful to us, have you?"

"Sorry?"

The dimples reappeared.

"I said... oh, what the heck, why leave it until tomorrow? Fancy going for a drink now?"

Who said life begins at forty? Let's make that thirty, shall we!

"Card shops reflect so many of life's major events, from the joyously happy to the desperately sad, it seemed a good starting point for a budding romance."

Just A Number

It takes a very special person indeed to distract Carrie from the impending trauma of her milestone birthday

By Linda Mitchelmore

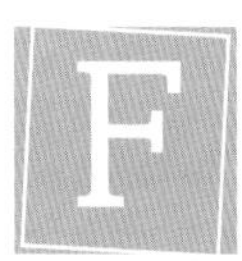

orty? It's just a number, Mum! OK?"

"Yes, but..." Carrie begins to reply, but Josh is already out of the door.

Carrie turns to her husband, Tom.

"I can't expect him to understand how I feel about turning forty, I suppose. He's only fifteen."

"Yeah – and forty probably sounds ancient to him."

"Well, thank you very much, not!" Carrie snaps. And then she, too, is out of the door. She needs space. She needs to think. No-one understands.

Certainly her mother doesn't.

"Why all the fuss, sweetheart?" she'd asked. "Getting old is a privilege, trust me – wrinkles and all."

"Have I got wrinkles, Mum?"

Carrie needed glasses to read these days but not to see herself in the mirror. She made a note to self never to look in the mirror with her glasses on.

"A few. I'd be surprised if you didn't and so should you be. Your living is in your face, and you had a lot of living when you were younger."

Carrie had changed the subject then – not wanting to be reminded of what a wild child she'd been in her teens.

Carrie walks briskly towards the park. Walking fast will burn off calories, won't it? At least, that's what all the magazines keep telling their readers. And that's another thing about turning forty – she doesn't seem to burn off calories quite as quickly these days as she used to.

When she moaned to her best friend about it, Amy said, "Hmm. Middle-aged spread. It isn't a sandwich filling, is it, Carrie? But yours sure is sticking to your hips the way too many sandwiches do."

So with the memory of that little non-compliment in her mind, Carrie begins to run. For fifteen seconds, twenty, twenty-five. She feels like the schoolgirl athlete she once was before she discovered make-up and discos and boys. But her breasts are no longer the pert and pointing-skywards little numbers in a

For twenty-five seconds she feels like the schoolgirl athlete she once was

Continued overleaf...

PICTURES: THINKSTOCK ILLUSTRATIONS: JIM DEWAR

Wrinkles? Where?

Continued from previous page

32A bra that they were in those days.

She stops running and trudges towards the outdoor café. Buys a black coffee. Ignores all the muffins she usually can't resist. Finds an empty table because she doesn't feel like talking to anyone today. Sits down.

A gaggle of small children and their mums arrive in the fenced-off enclosure that is the play area.

ALEX IS 4 TODAY proclaims a bright green balloon tied to the handle of a baby buggy. Carrie spots which one Alex is because he's wearing an oversized badge that says *I AM 4 TODAY.*

How important our age is – and what number – when we are children, she thinks. She remembers correcting her mother who, when asked how old Carrie was, had said, "She's seven." And Carrie had said – very indignantly – that no she wasn't, she was seven and a quarter!

An elderly, grey-haired lady, walking with a stick, comes over to sit at Carrie's table. The lady is smartly dressed. She looks as though she's come straight from the hairdresser – wash and set immaculate with not a single permed hair out of place.

Carrie makes a note to self – *never, ever have a perm and never, ever let the grey see the light of day.*

"Hello, dear," the lady says conversationally. "Come to watch your grandchildren play?"

Grandchildren? Carrie gulps.

"Er, no," she says. "Not yet."

Carrie makes another note to self – *never, ever throw a wild guess at a person's age. It's not a good idea.*

"Go on," the lady says with a teasing smile. "Guess my age."

Is this woman a mind-reader? Carrie is thrown quite off-balance, mentally, for a moment.

"Oh, I couldn't possibly…"

"Ninety-two! And I know – I don't look it, do I?"

"No," Carrie says and it's not a lie.

This ninety-two-year-old has more twinkle in her eye, more self-confidence than Carrie has at the moment. *Is that what growing old does for you?* she wonders. If so, she wants some.

"Actually," the lady says, "it's my birthday today. I'm going to buy a cake. I don't suppose you'd join me and have one, too, would you?"

The old lady presses her lips together and… is that a tear Carrie can see in her eye? She hasn't got anyone to share her birthday with, has she?

Carrie suddenly realises the lady doesn't have anyone to share her birthday with

"I'd love to. But…" Carrie takes the only coins she has from her pocket, places them on the table. "I'd like to treat you, but I only came out with the price of a coffee or two in my pocket."

"And you need cheering up. I can tell. I'm Ruby, by the way."

"Happy Birthday, Ruby. I'm Carrie."

Carrie makes another note to self – *never, ever let your low mood show in public.* She's lucky she's got such sprightly company, isn't she?

"So, dear," Ruby says, handing Carrie a ten-pound note, "perhaps I could ask you to go and get me a cup of tea and a blueberry muffin and whatever it is you'd

She's lucky to have such sprightly company

like for yourself. I can't manage a stick and a tray, I'm afraid."

And so an hour passes in Ruby's company. Carrie learns that Ruby comes to the park to see the children play. And there's always someone nice to talk to, she tells Carrie with a big grin.

Carrie makes her way home, her mood a little lighter for having met Ruby.

The front door is flung open as she walks up her path and Josh hurtles out.

"Where've you been?" he demands.

I could ask you the same, Carrie thinks. "To the park. For a walk. And a cup of coffee and a muffin. I met Ruby and..."

"Yeah, yeah," Josh says. "Dad says I've got to square it with you for some daft reason known only to himself, but... there's this all-night music gig I want to go to. I can go, can't I?"

"No," Carrie says, remembering her own wild-child days with a shudder. "Not this time. You're too young."

"But I'm nearly sixteen!"

"You're fifteen," Carrie corrects him.

"But, Mum..."

"And fifteen's just a number, Josh. OK?" She plonks a kiss on her son's cheek and skirts round him into the house.

She has decided to throw a party to celebrate her fortieth birthday. She's already invited Ruby.

There's lots to do...

THE AUTHOR SAYS...

"Age is just a number, Mum," my son said when I was given a bicycle for my fortieth. I'd never ridden before. That sentence still pops into my head if I'm worried about trying new things."

So Far Away

Anyone would be saddened by their child and grandchild emigrating – but for Max, there are deeper misgivings

By Della Galton

Max leaned in to the canvas and frowned. He'd been fiddling with the colour of the willows for a while but it still wasn't right. The sun was filtering in and out of a cloud bank, dappling the leaves so they kept changing colour. Maybe he should pack it in for the day – pray for more cloud. No – Caro wouldn't be happy. Unbroken sunshine, then?

He put down his brush and watched a trout break the surface of the river. The air was good down here, crisp and clear and sweet. He never tired of sucking it into his lungs. He never tired of the view.

A pain started off again deep in his heart and he tried to shrug it away.

In his pocket his phone buzzed.

"Hello, love," he said.

"I just wondered whether you were coming back for your lunch?"

Caro's voice had a thread of worry in it. He imagined her standing at the old range cooker, looking out of the window, scanning the path down to the river.

"I'll be back soon."

"It's no good fretting, Max. Holing yourself up down there brooding."

"I'm not brooding, I'm painting."

The shadow that passed across his heart was like those patterning the trees

That wasn't true. The paint was dry.

"You know what I mean. Angela's a grown woman. She has to make her own decisions, her own choices. We have to let her go, Max."

The shadow that passed over his heart was like the shadows patterning the trees.

Caro should have been the one aching over this – not him, but Caro had always been so practical, so down to earth, never a sentimentalist. That was one of the reasons he'd fallen in love with her. It was he, not Caro, who was a silly old fool.

Nevertheless she was right; he couldn't stay down here forever. It wasn't fair. He glanced back at the half-finished willows – he was never going to capture them anyway. He rolled up the canvas, packed away the paints. Art was something he'd always dabbled with, but had never had the time to get serious about. Then when they'd retired they'd bought the cottage, which had needed licking into shape, and now he finally had time to devote himself to painting, it wasn't as easy as he remembered. Maybe he was a fool to think he had any talent for art, either.

"I'm in here, love," Caro called as he slammed the back door and bent to put down his rucksack and easel.

PICTURES: SUPERSTOCK, THINKSTOCK ILLUSTRATIONS: JIM DEWAR

Angie had been before, many times, but...

He followed her voice through to the back room. She was on the sofa leafing through a book, a curl of her still-dark hair falling across her face. A plate of sandwiches covered in film wrap sat on the small table behind her.

"How did the painting go?"

"Not brilliant, to be honest. Have you had any lunch?"

"No, I thought I'd wait for you. I didn't do us much – had you remembered Angie and Nick were coming to dinner tonight?"

"I remembered." He flumped down beside her. "Are they bringing Stephen?"

"Yes, love, of course they're bringing Stephen." She turned dark eyes on him.

Continued overleaf...

Continued from previous page

"I want us to have a nice evening. No arguments, no bad feeling."

"Won't be any from me."

"No snide remarks about America."

"Nope."

"I mean it, Max. I want tonight to be special. I want them to know we respect their choices and we're happy for them."

He nodded irritably. "Fine. Although why they want to go to New York – of all places – I can't imagine."

She snapped her book shut so hard it startled him. "That's exactly what I mean. And I really can't see what you've got against the place."

"Oh, can't you!" He sat up a little straighter, frozen into annoyance. "Well, I'll tell you, shall I? New York's no place to bring up a child; all that smog and pollution and muggings every five minutes. No-one in their right minds would swap Devon for New York. It's ridiculous. It's – well, it's irresponsible."

She turned on him, her eyes blazing.

"It's perfectly safe where they're going. It's not as though Angie hasn't been before… lots of times. I just don't understand your problem."

He'd never seen her so angry. He moved back, the arm of the sofa hard against his hip.

"It's not really about New York, is it, Max? You'd be kicking up a fuss wherever they went, because it doesn't fit with your plans… Oh, I don't know what to say to you any more. But you are not going to spoil my last evening with my daughter and my grandson. You are NOT!"

It stung that she said "my" and not "our" but before he could respond, she was gone. A few moments later he heard the front door slam behind her.

Shocked, he crossed to the window and saw her getting into her car. There was a crunch of gravel – not quite a wheel spin – and she was gone.

She must be really mad with him. In all the years they'd been married he had never known her to storm off like that.

He picked up the book she'd been reading: *Your New Life In New York.* Pah! He flung it down again and a deep weariness gripped him.

Why couldn't he just tell Caro the truth? Why couldn't he tell her she was wrong about New York? If it had been anywhere else he'd have coped. OK, so he wouldn't have liked it – but somewhere other than New York would have been bearable.

For a moment he stared out at the empty space where his wife's car had been. Then he grabbed his coat and went out too. He headed back to the river. His wish for cloud had been granted – it was starting to rain.

Max was glad of the rain. It masked the tears that had begun to roll down his face.

"You are not going to spoil my last evening with them. You are NOT!"

It was almost five before he went back. There was an after-rain freshness in the air and the sun had come out. In places the land steamed gently. He had tried the house phone a couple of times, but Caro hadn't picked up so he guessed she was still out too.

She'd probably gone to see Marge, who was her boss in the book shop where she worked part time, and also her closest friend. Was it easier for women? Sometimes he wished he'd had someone to confide in – especially lately.

He could have confided in Caro, of course, but it was difficult, having never told her the truth about his past before. Actually he had tried once, early on, when Angie had first announced that her company had offered her a job out there.

"I really don't want them to go to New York," he'd said when his daughter had gone home. He'd started off quite meekly like that and Caro had patted his arm and said, "I don't want them to go either, love."

"No, what I mean is…"

"You were looking forward to spending more time with Stephen now he's old enough to take fishing – I know, love."

"Well, yes, but…"

"And this place is so perfect for grandchildren…" And she'd gone off into a whole spiel of how retirement would be so different without their only daughter, their only grandchild.

He'd given up then, pain swelling inside. Perhaps he should have tried harder to tell her the truth. But the words had always stuck in his throat, stuck in his heart.

Her car was back when he got to the house. The scent of cooking meat hit him as he went into the kitchen.

"I've done a beef wellington – their favourite." Caro didn't turn from the stove. "And there's apple crumble with crème fraiche. I expect she's on a diet and it's not quite as fattening as cream."

"I'm sorry," he said, standing just inside the doorway, watching the evening sunlight shimmer her hair.

"So you've come to your senses." She turned and he saw the tell-tale paleness of her face and knew she'd been crying too. How had he ever let it get to this?

"Leave that a minute," he said.

He thought she might refuse – beef wellington was tricky – but maybe she was at a good point to leave it. Or maybe something in his voice touched her.

She came across the flagstones and he put his hands on her lower arms, squeezing lightly. "I need to tell you something."

They sat at the kitchen table and he plunged in before he could change his mind.

"In 1937 my uncle and my grandparents emigrated to New Jersey."

She nodded. She knew that part.

He paused. It was still difficult, even though he'd made up his mind, to tell her the rest.

"My mother planned to join them, but she didn't want to leave straight away. She had quite a good job at the time. She was working as a housekeeper and didn't want to let down the family – they had always been good to her, so she planned to join her parents and brother later."

Caro glanced at him curiously.

"In 1938 she got pregnant with me, as you know…"

Another quick nod, but her eyes were softer than when he'd started. She could hear from his voice how hard this was.

"The family she was working for threw

Continued overleaf…

Continued from previous page

her out – she wasn't married, see, and that was a heinous crime in those days."

He paused again. It was hard to breathe. His heart was thumping so hard he was dizzy. "She never did get married. My father said he wanted nothing more to do with her."

Caro reached across and put her hand lightly over his. But she didn't interrupt, and she didn't ask why he'd lied for all these years about his father being a decorated war hero who'd died when he was four, and he was grateful for that.

"Mother decided it would be a good time to join her family, so she applied for immigration. In those days anyone wanting to live in the United States had to go in via Ellis Island. They wanted people, you see. They wanted workers.

"The health checks were pretty cursory – they wanted to know you weren't going to drop down dead on their doorstep or spread any contagious diseases, but other than that you were pretty much in."

Caro looked at him. He swallowed hard.

"She had just enough money for her passage to Ellis Island – after that she was going to stay with her family, my grandparents. But the authorities wouldn't let her in."

"But why not?" Caro's voice was softly indignant and he loved her for that. "She wasn't ill."

"No, but she was pregnant and they didn't believe she'd be able to support herself. Not on her own. Not being a single parent."

"But what about her family?"

"My uncle Harry was supporting my grandparents already – my grandfather hadn't found it as easy to get work as he'd expected. The authorities decided Harry wouldn't be able to support another person – potentially another two people." He broke off.

"So what happened?"

"She was deported back to England. She was all alone, virtually penniless, and with me on the way. Can you imagine how that must have felt; how terrified she would have been?"

He knew he had tears pouring down his face again, but it no longer mattered. It was as if the pain of years was emptying out of his heart and it was a relief.

"Oh my poor, dear love."

He wasn't aware of either of them moving, but somehow she was beside him. He was in her arms. He was no longer alone.

For a long while, nothing else was said. Then slowly he became aware of the smell of something burning.

"Oh, good grief, the wellington."

"Stuff the wellington." Caro's voice was teary. He looked at her in surprise.

"But it's their favourite."

"We'll have fish and chips." She was getting up, slightly unsteadily, and he watched her move across to the oven and open the door.

"Is it ruined? I'm sorry."

"Don't you dare apologise." She moved the smoking baking tray with its blackened lump to the top of the stove and turned to face him. "It's me who should be apologising. I should have known you weren't being difficult. I should have realised it was deeper."

She swiped at her face with her hand.

He got up. "Don't cry, love. I should have told you before. I was ashamed to tell you. I was ashamed to tell anyone the truth about my father."

"No wonder you didn't want them to go to America. No wonder."

"I was being childish." He sighed deeply. "They wouldn't take my mother, so I didn't see why they should have my daughter. Just because it suited them. Just because she's smart and beautiful. I didn't see why they should bloody well pick and choose."

"Oh Max. That's not being childish. It's being human." She tripped over his paint box and the canvas he'd started that morning unrolled itself on the floor. Caro bent to pick it up. "Hey, that's not bad."

"I couldn't get the tops of the willows right – the light kept changing."

"They look fine to me. Anyway, it's practice, isn't it? You can't expect to get it perfect first time. Painting's a skill you have to learn. You could do a course."

"Maybe." He wished there was a course he could do on communication – or was it courage he needed?

"Do you think I should tell Angie the truth? She must have thought I was an obstreperous old sod."

"She knows that already." She smiled. "I'm joking. Don't look so shocked. Besides," she went on, moving closer and thumbing a tear from his cheek. "Not wanting them to go is understandable."

He nodded. "All those fishing trips I was going to take Stephen on. The fun we were going to have in the summer – the camp building, the hiking…"

"We can still do those things – it's only six hours. We are going to see them again." She smiled, her eyes full of hope. "And don't forget New York isn't forever. Maybe Angie's company will move them back in a couple of years."

"Maybe." He felt lighter. He wasn't sure whether it was the sharing of a secret so long buried, or just the fact that she was right. Nothing was forever. He hadn't thought any of it through. He hadn't thought beyond his prejudice.

"Should I tell her? She must have thought me an obstreperous old sod"

The doorbell jangled.

"Oh my goodness, that's them – and here's us with nothing but burnt offerings."

"I'll go and get the chips," he said. "I'll be back before you know it."

She caught his hand, and he turned. "I'll go a bit later," he said, his voice cracking a little as he looked into Caro's clear blue eyes; saw the love there. He didn't need a course on courage. All that he needed was right here.

"Before I go," he added softly, "I need to talk to our daughter."

THE AUTHOR SAYS…

"I was inspired to write this story after a holiday to New York. We visited Ellis Island while we were there and I found the history absolutely fascinating and very moving."

Jack's Way

Even setting off from a totally different starting point, our determined boy had the makings of a true champion…

By Tess Niland Kimber

nly sometimes does it catch me – as it does today, as I'm standing at the kitchen sink, haunted by a bad attack of what Dave calls "the might-have-beens".

I'm washing up the breakfast things, a soapy mug frozen in time in my wet hands, as I look out of the window over our long, narrow garden. Although I know it'll hurt, that tears will be misting my eyes before I can put this mug on the drainer, I can't help but imagine how our Jack might have charged up and down the lawn or, maybe, climbed the arthritic apple tree over by the trellis.

Dave, in the old jeans he keeps for gardening, might have stood at the base, wagging his finger, trying hard not to catch Jack's infectious smile; a smile that makes telling off almost impossible.

Is it the promise of spring filling me with hope – or Jack's surprise for his dad?

Yes, that catch in my throat and the pinch of pain are there today, reminding me of how much life is like that piece I love by Emily Perl Kingsley; you know, the one that says parents like Dave and I somehow arrived by accident in "Holland" the day we had our Jack, although we'd been packed and excited, expecting to land with all the other expectant Mums and Dads in "Italy".

Over the years, though, we've not only got used to "Holland" but we've grown to love it. It's different here, but no less beautiful.

Just sometimes, like today, though, that pain jabs its blade into me again until I remember… remember that there are challenges here that I sometimes fear we can't meet.

I take a deep breath and watch a robin pick its way daintily across the frost-twinkling lawn, a pink worm sandwiched in its beak. Daffodils are standing proud along the border by the fence and I feel the freshness of it all, as if the garden is starting to come alive again after the long chill of winter.

Yet is it the promise of spring that has me full of hope today, or the surprise Jack's planned for Dave's birthday? He's fifty today – unbelievable.

"Mum?"

Suddenly, as if he's read my mind, I hear the click-click that heralds Jack's every step. I turn and smile as he totters over and presses himself close; his own personal cue that he wants another cuddle. You see, if he's walking with his

Continued overleaf…

PICTURES: ISTOCKPHOTO, THINKSTOCK ILLUSTRATIONS: KIRK HOUSTON

The daffodils seemed to symbolise hope and a fresh start

Continued from previous page

sticks, he can't put his arms around me first or he'll lose his balance. So he does it this way – Jack's way.

"I'm not surprised you need a hug today. I think it's going to be a day made for cuddles." I squeeze him tight. "And don't worry if you can't manage it. Just having you here is a big enough present for me and your Dad."

It's not just a big day for Dave; it is for our son, too. He's been working towards this for weeks, now. Years, really…

"Don't worry, I'm going to do it, Mum," he says, tilting his smooth face up to me, wide blue eyes – the image of Dave's – shining with marathon-runner determination. "For Dad."

"Well, just go –"

" – careful!" he finishes for me, sighing and morphing into Victor Meldrew before my very eyes. "It's OK – I will, but I'll do it my way."

Now he sounds like Frank Sinatra…

I can't help but smile, my face as tight as if it's been sunburned and proud tears are threatening to hurtle down my cheeks like a Paralympic skier.

Over the last ten years, most things have had to be done "Jack's way". All three of us have had to learn to adjust and attempt what's usually deemed routine, in different ways.

And you know what? It's been fun to turn the downright impossible into a challenge and then, more often than not, into a success.

If only I'd known how good it would be, I wouldn't have been so frightened and sad, I think, watching as Jack makes his way over to his chair at the kitchen table. There's a couple of wrapped presents and some cards, waiting for Dave to open when he comes in from his night shift at the bakery.

But the biggest surprise isn't wrapped up, and he'll find it later in the garden…

In those early days, after Jack was born, the pain was like having neat bleach poured into a paper cut, as the idea of what should have been was stripped away – hope by hope. But now I've learned to enjoy every moment.

I stand and wait, torn between wanting to protect Jack and letting him try this

Okay, we might have missed the big milestones but the pleasure of having each stage broken into tiny steps has meant that we've been able to celebrate all the more.

"Jack might not have survived his birth," Dave would often say, mopping my tears with his cloth handkerchief. "That's quite a baseline to head up from, Nikki."

He's totally right, of course, but even so, it took time for us to stop grieving for "Italy" and rejoice in the Jack – the "Holland" – we do have.

As he plays a game on my mobile, his thin arms resting on the pine table, I think that if anyone has taught me this, it's Jack himself. At first, I'd been holding his hand but more often than not now, it's our son who pulls me along through life.

"Yay! I've beaten my top score – again." He cheers.

Now I only wonder at all the things he can do, how hard he tries, and how lucky we are to share this special "Holland" of our own with him.

The sticks are like a kiss on the grass

Later that morning, the watery March sun filters through the trees like a ghost, splaying its fingers over frost-burned grass.

I stand and wait, torn between wanting to protect Jack and letting him try this. What if failure crushes him like a cigarette butt under a stiletto?

"You ready, Bob?" Jack calls to our smiley, grey-haired neighbour who's come round to our garden for this special event.

"Ready? I've been waiting all week for this, lad." He laughs, putting a carrier bag down by the bench.

Jack had roped Bob in to help. They've always had a special bond and, as Jack said, "We'll need someone to count."

"Well, I could do it."

"Mum – you can't. You'll be all teary and embarrassing."

So graciously I'd conceded that Bob should be chief adjudicator.

"Thirty?" Jack checks with him.

Thirty – it's such a funny amount. Not memorable like 1066 or unlucky like thirteen or even important like twenty-one. But I've a feeling that this number thirty could mean the world to Dave; to us both.

"This is exciting," Dave says, looking tired from his shift as he joins Bob and me on the path.

"It's for your birthday, Dad, remember. From me. I didn't know what else to get you," Jack says, standing on the grass, his sticks either side of him like guards.

"You didn't need to get me anything. I've got you, son – so I don't need anything else, do I?" He smiles warmly.

Jack's back is slightly bent and his knees touch in that classic pose. The paralysis is the enemy within that we fight each night with stretches and gaiters and silent swear words. It pulls his body out of shape, but his heart and mind into gear. He won't let his disability beat him – that's just not his way.

"Come on, lad. You can do this," Bob encourages.

Jack's blue eyes hold us in his gaze for a brief moment. Then, once he has his balance, he casts his sticks to the ground. They land crossed – looking like a giant kiss painted on the sunlit grass.

Rolling slightly, he heaves his thin body to one side and then starts to step without his sticks.

The second Dave realises what Jack's planned, he squeezes my hand and mentally, I begin to count. Bob, looking as serious as any World Cup referee, mouths the numbers I can hear all too clearly in my head.

Continued overleaf...

Continued from previous page

One, two, three…

I'm willing Jack so hard, it's as if I'm walking beside him, holding his hand. But I can't take any of the credit; he's doing this alone. His way…

Fifteen, sixteen, seventeen …

I can barely dare to breathe. He might never be able to run or ride a bike or jump on a skateboard, but no-one can tell me that this isn't just as much of an achievement; and just as exciting to witness.

"He'll do it, Nikki," Dave whispers. "He's been winning since the day he was born, our lad."

Twenty-three, twenty-four…

Jack totters and sways but I can't really see him. Tears stream as my heart leaps from my chest to my mouth. Is he going to fall? No… he stops for a second and regains his balance before taking some more steps.

Twenty-six, twenty-seven…

As he walks further into the distance, I don't see the toddler or boy that can't. I see our own, home-grown hero – the boy who taught himself to stand; the boy who found a way to use a slide – and suddenly as he walks away, I see the man he will one day grow into…

Goodness, what a person he'll be! Nothing in life will ever be easy for Jack but he'll always get there – his way.

Twenty-nine… thirty!

Oh my God, thirty!

"Oh, Jack!" I yell. My tears cross the finish line with him as I rush to hug him.

"Mum – what a show-up!" he moans through a mile-wide smile.

"What a birthday present! Oh, well done, Jack." Dave beams, tears dripping off the end of his nose, as he takes over hugging duty from me.

"Yes, congratulations, lad," Bob says, grinning from ear to ear. "You more than did it! I declare a new Jack record. That was thirty-three steps."

He walks over to the bench and from the carrier bag, pulls out a massive bar of chocolate.

"It might be your Dad's birthday, but you deserve this." Bob ruffles his blond hair affectionately.

"I did it!" he whispers, the effort clear in his voice. "I've been practising for weeks to show Dad, haven't I, Mum?"

This time, devoid of sticks, he can hug me. No longer the boy that can't, but the champion who can.

Yes, he did it. Not as smoothly or as quickly as you or I would. He had to do it his way – Jack's way.

I gaze at our family on this special day and I realise how firmly I now live in "Holland" – and you know what? There's nowhere I'd rather live in the whole, wide, world…

I see our own home-grown hero – and suddenly I see the man he will grow into

THE AUTHOR SAYS…

"Parenthood hasn't been anything like we expected, but the children have brought us deeper joy than we'd ever thought possible. This story is based on my own son's achievements."

Fancy That!

Purple facts that make you go **"Wow!"**

◆ Purple is a colour often well-liked by very creative or eccentric types, and is the favorite colour of adolescents.

◆ **In Thailand, purple is worn by a widow mourning her husband's death.**

◆ A "purple heart" is a US military decoration for soldiers wounded or killed in battle.

◆ **Violet has the shortest wavelength of the spectrum and behind it is the invisible ultraviolet.**

The scent of lavender is said to be stress reducing

In Tibet, amethyst is considered to be sacred to Buddha and rosaries are often fashioned from it

◆ **Purple was the colour of the first dye created by man. Called mauveine and made out of coal tar, the recipe was discovered by William Henry Perkin in 1856.**

◆ Purple is the colour of the highest denomination poker chip: $5,000.

◆ **Born to the Purple: a person who is born into a noble or royal family.**

◆ Purple Prose is an elaborately written poem or paragraph in literature.

Purple wisteria has an amazing scent often associated with romance

◆ **In Japan the colour purple signifies wealth and position.**

◆ Leonardo da Vinci believed that the power of meditation increases ten times when done in a purple light.

◆ **Purple denotes virtue and faith in Egypt.**

Purple represents the planet Jupiter

WORDS: BABS BEATON PICTURES: THINKSTOCK, ISTOCKPHOTO, ALAMY

One Step At A Time

The path to love is never smooth – and can stub your toes, as Amy knows too well!

By Margaret Mounsdon

Do feet talk? Amy sighed aloud. For a tutor, Greg had some pretty strange ideas for thinking outside the box. How on earth was she supposed to come up with a two thousand word essay on that one?

"Hi there, toes." Amy wriggled them through the gap in her peep-toe red stilettos. "Nothing to say?"

The delicate shade of oyster shell pink varnish caught the evening sunlight. Amy liked painting her nails. It was the one beauty treatment that gave immediate results. You painted your toenails, you felt good. Result.

Amy sighed, still looking at her toes. "You're no help with my coursework," she lectured them.

Amy hoped a change of scenery would help stimulate her imagination

She had hoped a change of scenery would stimulate her imagination into coming up with words of wisdom that would satisfy her tutor. So far, though, she was out of luck.

The park bench shifted beneath her. Amy's eyes swept up from her feet to the man now sitting at the far end. She tucked a strand of dark hair behind her ears, adjusted her laptop and tried to look busy.

"Talking to yourself?" The newcomer smiled. "Always a bad sign."

"I wasn't talking to myself," Amy retaliated before she remembered stranger danger.

She began gathering up her work. The

PICTURES: THINKSTOCK ILLUSTRATIONS: MANDY MURRAY

This assignment was proving harder than she thought

park attracted some odd people at twilight and it looked as if she might have pulled a weirdo. He wasn't wearing a raincoat… but that meant nothing these days.

"Not leaving on my account, are you?" he asked.

Amy swung her bag over her shoulder and without another word strode across the grass towards the gates.

Her feet were talking to her now. They were telling her to get out of there.

The lights in Toni's café twinkled; a beacon of safety. Amy pushed the door. A sea of steamy warmth welcomed her.

Continued overleaf…

Continued from previous page

"Ciao, bella." Toni kissed his fingers.

"The usual please, Toni."

"Subito. Coming up."

Amy sat down at a window seat. She was breathing heavily. Because of that wretched man, she still hadn't started her essay. If she didn't have anything down on paper, Greg would be furious. He'd already accused her of wasting his time when she'd missed her last two tutorials because of Jon.

Jon's trainers had done some pretty mean talking. *A jog round the park,* he had said. So how come his feet weren't blistered from wearing new trainers? And why were there no grass stains on them? It hadn't taken Amy long to suss out that the only jogging he'd done was round to his old girlfriend's flat.

Soon after that, his feet had had their final say to her, by crashing down the stairs and out of her life.

Amy had spent most of last week writing Jon out of her life, instead of writing her essay.

The fragrant aroma of a cappuccino with extra sprinkles wafted under her nostrils. She looked down at Toni's feet. He wore EU-approved footwear, with reinforced leather uppers and special non-slip soles.

"Cara mia." He beamed at her. "You be my girl?"

"Ah, maybe next week, Toni."

They both knew perfectly well that neither of them meant a word of it, but it was fun to play the game.

"So what is it this week, your work?" Toni asked as he glanced at the blank document on the screen in front of Amy.

"An essay on feet."

Toni raised his eyes. "My feet, they ache after standing on them all day. Last thing I wanna do is write about them."

He put down her bun and the cappuccino and left her to it.

The doorbell pinged. Amy glanced over; it was the man from the park. He smiled at her. Amy turned away, opened her bag and got out her scribbled notes. A stalker she did not need.

Toni didn't mind if she occasionally used his café for work.

"One day you write the next Harry Potter." He would laugh. "Then I want my share in your fortune."

Amy tried to relax and clear her mind. Usually it helped the words flow, but it wasn't working today.

She chewed her lip. What sort of feet would Romeo Montague have? He was young and nimble enough to engage in a sword fight. She imagined his long, lean limbs, encased in red tights.

Hunched over her table and in-between nibbles of bun and sips of coffee, Amy began to fill the screen with text. Greg had offbeat ideas, but they certainly worked the brain. Why had she never realised that the nurse in *Romeo and Juliet* probably had corns and limped? And as for Friar Lawrence, if he had been a younger, fitter man with feet to match, the greatest love tragedy in the world might never have happened.

A tapping on the window drew Amy's attention away from her work. Her ex,

"I'm sorry if I scared you, only I'm new in town and feeling a bit lonely"

He smiled over at Amy, only to be ignored

Jon, stood outside. He was smiling confidently and making jogging gestures, inviting her to join him. His feet were going up and down. Were they still telling lies? Amy didn't care any more. She turned her attention back to her essay.

A chair scraped the floor beside her.

"Excuse me." The park man smiled hesitantly. "I want to apologise," he said. "I'm sorry if I scared you, only I'm new in town and feeling a bit lonely." He hesitated. "It was a pants chat-up line, wasn't it, that thing about talking to yourself? Accusing you of going mad? Can't believe I really said it."

In the welcoming warmth of Toni's bar, he didn't look scary at all. Jon began tapping on the window again. Amy continued to ignore him and smiled at the man from the park. Now she came to look at him properly, he had quite nice feet. So what if he was wearing suede loafers? They were her dad's favourite shoes – and Dad's feet had never, ever cheated on Mum.

"Sit down," Amy patted the chair, "and tell me your name."

"It's Dan."

"Hello, Dan. I like your shoes," Amy replied with a smile.

THE AUTHOR SAYS...

"I was sitting on the grass in the park near some sunbathing students, one of whom had painted a smiley blue face on the underneath of her big toe. It made me smile!"

Out Of The Blue

When the worst happens, is it possible that true love and technology might somehow reach across the divide?

By Linda Gruchy

Sarah's computer was winking at her. As she expected, it was Tony on Messenger.

"Leaving work now, love," he typed. "Home in about an hour. Ttfn. x"

"Love you too xx," she typed back.

Sarah had busied herself happily in the kitchen chopping vegetables, when all of a sudden she noticed the orange tab on the computer flashing again, indicating another message.

Oh no, I bet he's been delayed, she thought with a frown, and clicked on his new message.

"Sorry, love. It wasn't my fault. I tried to hang on but it was too late. I love you – always remember that."

The doorbell rang. Two police officers stood on the front step, caps in hand

How weird was that?

The doorbell rang. Two police officers stood on the front step, caps in hand.

"Are you Sarah Burridge?"

Sarah nodded.

"It's about Tony. I'm afraid we have some bad news."

Later, when the police officers had gone, Sarah sat down at the computer, heart a lump of solid ice.

"I can't believe it," she murmured aloud, staring at Tony's precious last words. On impulse, she typed into the Messenger box. "Oh Tony – I'm going to miss you so much."

She started to shiver when a reply appeared. "I'll miss you too, my love."

Hope raged through her body, but then the truth hit her; someone must be playing silly jokes on Tony's work computer, didn't know Tony was dead, probably thought it a right laugh.

"But you're *dead.* The police have just been," she typed, sending the message with a vicious stab at the return key.

"I know. I'm sorry." A sad emoticon.

Sorry? *Sorry?*

"Is this a joke?" she typed furiously.

"No, love. No it's not. I wish it was, lol."

"So how come you're typing to me?"

"I don't know. My laptop was in the car, and I've got it with me now. I think it got broken along with me."

Continued overleaf...

All she had now
was words

Continued from previous page

"Where are you?" she typed.

"Here. In the room with you. On the sofa. Can't you see me?"

"No." Sarah turned and squinted at the sofa, just to be sure. "What's it like, being… well, you know?"

"Odd. Like being in a dream."

"I'm afraid to log off. Am I suffering from shock or something?" she typed. A sob caught in her throat. "No, this can't be real. Whoever you are, this is a very sick joke."

"Ask me a question only I would know the answer to," typed Tony.

"OK then. What was your mother's middle name?" typed Sarah after a few minutes' thought.

"Deirdre. Her name was Joan Deirdre Smith, nee Collins, born November 12, 1946, died…" the typing paused for a moment. "… December 3, 2010. You were a wonderful comfort to me then, my love. You made it bearable."

Correct, every word of it.

This was real then, if still unbelievable. Nobody could know all that.

"But who's going to be my comforter? I've got nobody now; only you. I don't know what to do when someone dies.

"Is that why you're still here?" she typed. "To help me, guide me, I mean?"

"There's something more important to do but I don't know what, yet. Will you phone my cousin Penny and tell her the bad news, please?"

"OK." Sarah remembered Penny from Joan's funeral a couple of years back, a terrifyingly efficient businesswoman who lived miles away in Scotland. Tony and Sarah hardly saw anything of her, just exchanging letters at Christmas.

"I wish I knew Penny better. We really are dreadful at the sociable things, aren't we?" she typed.

"I know love, but then, we only ever needed each other. Thank you for four wonderful years."

Sarah found Penny's phone number, dialled. A cool, calming voice answered.

"Penny? It's Sarah. Something awful's happened…"

Tony had typed, "ttfn love," and slipped offline by the time Sarah had finished talking.

Next morning, after a sleepless night, Sarah pushed back the curtains and saw a large Audi parked outside. Penny. Sarah rushed down the stairs and flung open the door just as Penny was about to press the doorbell.

"I drove all night." Penny's eyes were rimmed with fatigue.

"Come in, I'll put the kettle on," exclaimed Sarah, eyeing up the bag Penny was holding.

So many things they had discussed, meaning to get round to them one day

Penny gave Sarah a hug. "Poor you. I've come to stay for a few days to help you through the awful necessities."

Sarah made a pot of strong real coffee, put a few digestives on a plate and they nibbled and sipped while discussing what needed to be done. Sarah couldn't believe how calmly they were talking, how matter-of-fact, and was getting more and more reassured about the horrible practicalities when Penny said, "Where's Tony's will?"

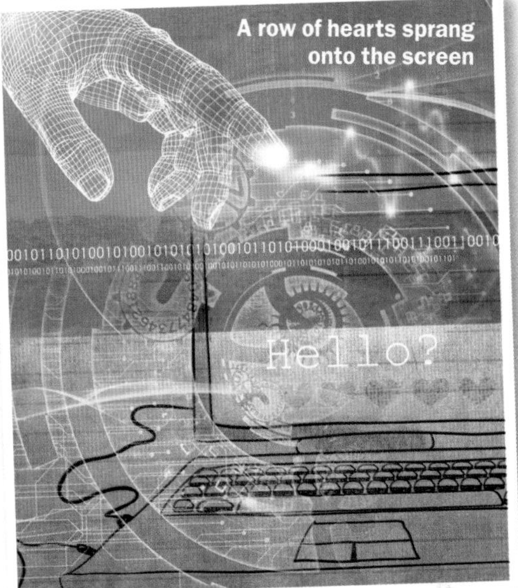

A row of hearts sprang onto the screen

"Oh! I don't know. I'm not sure whether he ever made one."

It was one of the things they'd meant to get round to some day.

Penny fiddled with her cup before saying, "This is rather a delicate question, but did you ever, um… tie the knot?"

That was another thing they'd discussed, meaning to get round to it some day, but never did.

Sarah shook her head. "Not exactly."

"Oops," said Penny. She sipped her coffee a few times before adding, "I hate to mention it on top of everything else, but this is important. If Tony didn't make a will then he's intestate, and that means his estate goes to his relatives. And unless you married him, then you're not a relative and don't have an automatic claim on his estate. It can get very messy and we don't want that. I'll bet he never thought to make you part owner of this house, did he?"

Sarah shook her head. It was another thing he'd never got round to. They hadn't felt any urgency – why should they?

"I can't cope with this," she wailed. "It's all too much."

"I know." Penny laid a comforting hand on Sarah's. "That's why I'm here. To help." She stifled a yawn. "But first, I could do with a quick power nap."

While Penny was dozing in the spare room Sarah tried to do as Penny had instructed; to rack her brains over the matter of the will. She typed, "Are you there, Tony?"

His status changed from Offline to Away. "Yes – tired though. Thin."

"Did you make a will, please, love?"

"Yes. I left the house to you."

"Thank goodness. I was terrified of suddenly finding myself homeless at my age – and, Tony, I have some very surprising news. You're going to be a daddy. I was going to tell you last night when you got home, but…"

"Wow! Oh my love, that's fantastic!" A row of heart emoticons sprang onto the screen.

"Fantastic, but scary. I'd given up hope. Oh no – your words are fading. They're a much paler blue."

"Must rest."

"The will, darling, where is it, please?"

But Tony had slipped offline.

The police came round with some of Tony's personal effects like his watch, phone, wallet and his laptop computer. The watch and phone still worked, but the computer was broken when she plugged it in.

What would she do if she couldn't find the will, especially in her condition? She

Continued overleaf…

Continued from previous page

placed her hands over her tummy. Precious, so precious. Thank goodness she'd been able to tell Tony about it even if he was… She stared at the ceiling, at the cracks they'd meant to fix one of these days, as familiar as the laughter lines in Tony's face.

I'm grieving, I'm in shock. I shouldn't have to be trying to make rational decisions on sorting my life out, she thought.

Penny was still snoozing and Sarah was about to take her a cuppa when she noticed her computer was winking orange.

"Thank goodness," Tony wrote. "You need to keep my laptop charged up for me to type. The battery was flat earlier. The will is in the strongbox."

"What strongbox?"

"I haven't a clue, I'm afraid."

"What does it look like? How big is it, for starters?" asked Penny.

"I don't know. I'll see if I can find out," said Sarah. She rushed indoors, and typed, "You there, Tony? What's the strongbox like, please? The garage is a bit cluttered and it's not easy to find something when we don't even know what we're looking for."

"Hi there, love. It's like a big briefcase size, fireproof and very heavy. I'll see if I can find a pic." Suddenly the screen filled with a photograph. "Like that. I think it's near the tool cupboard. And watch your back when you pick it up. It weighs a ton."

Sarah hurried back out to the garage. "It's a lot smaller than I expected and it should be by the tool cupboard."

"Five minutes ago you hadn't a clue. It's as if you went and asked someone"

Did they have a strongbox?

"In the garage."

"OK. Ta. I'll look right now."

"Feeling faint," wrote Tony in blue. "Speak later." He slipped offline again.

There is a will and it's in a strongbox somewhere in the garage," said Sarah as she handed Penny a cup of tea.

"Oh – well remembered."

"Good grief." Penny gasped as they opened the garage door. "It's stuffed. Didn't Tony ever sort this lot out? Don't tell me; he was intending to get round to it one day. Where's this strongbox then?"

Sure enough, there was the box.

"It's heavy," added Sarah.

Penny looked at her quizzically. "Have you any idea how strange this seems?" she asked. "Five minutes ago you hadn't a clue, yet now you know exactly what it looks like and where it is. It's as if you went and asked someone."

"Penny, this is going to sound loopy… I did ask someone. I asked Tony. Let me show you…

"Tell me I'm not going mad; tell me you can talk to Tony too," pleaded Sarah, showing Penny her entire conversation on the computer.

"I can't see anything," said Penny, shaking her head.

"So I am going nuts then." Sarah chewed her knuckle.

"N-no," said Penny thoughtfully. "Not mad. Though grief can do strange things. Perhaps it's your subconscious remembering things."

But Sarah wanted to believe it was Tony. It *had* to be him. Her thoughts must have been plain because Penny added, "Maybe Tony can only talk to you."

"She's right, my love," typed Tony. "So is the will there in the box?"

"I don't know. Not looked yet. Where's the key?" typed Sarah.

"I can see your writing," said Penny, eyes round as a cat's. "But then it disappears. What's going on?"

"You're not nuts, this is me," typed Tony, adding a stern smiley face. "The key is in the vase on the mantelpiece."

"Did you see that?" Sarah demanded. Tony's just told me where the key is."

"Nope – can't see anything. Say 'hi' to Tony for me, though."

"Say 'hi' back," typed Tony. "Now, go check that the will is where I think it is. I can't rest until I know you've got it safe."

There were several keys in the vase, and the fifth one fitted. Inside the strongbox were several important documents – and the will.

"Good," said Penny, reading it. "He's left you the house, and there's a life insurance policy to pay for… incidentals. Oh… how lovely; he's left me Auntie Joan's jewellery."

"Do you mind Tony leaving me the house? If he hadn't made the Will, you'd have inherited it, wouldn't you?" asked Sarah suddenly, face burning.

"Silly; of course not. You meant the world to Tony, and it's only right and proper you should have it."

"I haven't got much time left now. This is it, my beloved. Truly goodbye…"

"I'd better tell Tony." Sarah went to the computer and typed, "We found it OK, thanks. Penny's thrilled about the jewellery."

"Good," replied Tony. "Penny's a good friend. Maybe she will be Godmother. That would be nice."

"Your writing's gone pale again." Sarah cast an anxious glance at Tony's broken laptop. "Is it charging properly?"

"No. I haven't much time left. I want you to remember the four wonderful years we had."

"I love you," typed Sarah.

"I love you too. Now unplug my laptop because it's overheating. This is it, my beloved. Truly goodbye."

A hot smell wafted in front of Sarah. She unplugged Tony's laptop in a panic, then turned back to her computer. As she watched, her conversation box slowly faded, then vanished altogether.

THE AUTHOR SAYS…

"My hubby often uses online messaging to tell me when he's leaving work. If he's late, I sometimes (rather morbidly) think how awful it would be if he didn't make it home."

The Gift of Time

When you think you have to let go, but know that you just can't, perhaps you'll find that you don't have to after all

By Elaine Peake

o you believe in ghosts? Not the chain rattling, moaning apparitions that roam the corridors of failing public houses and crumbling stately homes.

My particular phantom lives in my peripheral vision, just out of focus. It is the shadow that dances in candlelight, the feather light brush of invisible hair across my cheek. It is the cool breath of wind that coils around me in an airless stuffy room, the familiar perfume that I know so well. It may be mere coincidence, all I know for certain is that it comforts me in her absence.

The steam from the shower thinned slightly, revealing my black fine woollen skirt suit and grey silk blouse hanging from the rail. The few stubborn creases that had refused to drop out were imperceptible thanks to the warm, moist air.

I was so angry with Mum when she told me she was dying. I felt as though it was her fault, as though she had somehow invited those killer cells into her body, with no thought for what it would mean to me, just as she had invited every new experience, every challenge into her life.

I knew I would always have to share her with the rest of the world, but I was happy to live in her shadow, to feel the warmth of her reflected glory, although I found it difficult to admit that I needed her help sometimes.

When my first boyfriend dumped me in favour of someone a little more generous with her favours, she told me that my taste in men would undoubtedly improve with age and that she had kissed many frogs before meeting my father.

I had sat behind her on the edge of the huge bed that she had slept in alone since my father's death, watching her through the dressing table mirror as she carefully applied her favourite tangerine lipstick. As she left the house that evening to give a talk at the local women's refuge, I knew she didn't really understand.

She was right of course about my taste in men improving. Geoff adored her almost

It was difficult to take in just how ill she was; she was essentially still my mum

PICTURES: ISTOCKPHOTO, THINKSTOCK ILLUSTRATIONS: MANDY MURRAY

as much as I did. This was mainly because, if he and I rowed she would almost always, and much to my annoyance, take his side. That and the fact that she always cooked him a proper breakfast fry up whenever he stayed over.

I should have seen the signs; the sudden weight loss, the early nights, late mornings and the general lack of enthusiasm for life that was so unlike her.

It was only after she had collapsed at work for the second time in a week that I became really concerned.

She said nothing; it was Evelyn, her manager who had phoned me because she was worried. Unable to ignore the obvious any longer, I bullied her into seeing the doctor, but something told me even before the results of the tests that it was going to be the worst possible news.

She refused chemotherapy and radiotherapy on the grounds that she wanted some quality of life for whatever quantity she had left, and with the help of painkillers, she made the very most of her good days.

It was difficult to take in at first. Her

Continued overleaf...

Continued from previous page

shoulder length auburn hair had lost none of its vibrancy. She was a little more slender, a touch more alabaster in her skin tone, there was a hint of shadow under her eyes, but essentially she was still my mum, and it was easy to forget just how ill she really was.

Geoff and I had arranged to renew our wedding vows just before Christmas. We decided to bring it forward and, predictably, Mum was appalled at this change of plan. I explained to her on that rainy Monday as we shared a morning cuppa, that I simply couldn't and wouldn't do it without her being there.

My dress was easy to choose in comparison to hers and despite my pleas to the contrary, she eventually plumped for a huge diaphanous salmon pink creation that Barbara Cartland would have envied. I'm so glad that she ignored my protests and stuck to her guns. With the sunlight behind her on the photographs, she looked every inch the Hollywood film star and I was thrilled to be sharing centre stage with her.

For a few cherished weeks afterwards and while she was still fairly well, we probably spent more time together than at any other since my childhood. We talked for hours. I reminded her of the huge fuss she made over my birthday every year. Big wonky cakes covered in sweets and candles that she had baked herself. Everything was oversized and fabulous, just like her. She had loved to be in the limelight, but she never really understood, until then, my need to stay in the shade.

We talked about Dad too in those weeks; properly and fully for the first time in the twenty-five years since he had passed away. I was thirteen at the time and I thought that I would die of sadness, but in spite of how terribly she was hurting, she had put my grief before her own.

She would get up with me in the middle of the night when dreams and shadows filled me with fear, and take me into the safety of her bed. Together we would look through old photograph albums, fingering the yellowing snapshots. I would trace the outline of my father's smiling face as my mother stifled her own tears.

Just as I was coming to terms with her illness, she started to fade rapidly, diminishing in both size and substance until I hardly recognised her any more. Precious moments of lucidity became fewer and her death, when it finally came, was swift and painless.

I promised her there'd be no tears at the funeral and hastily brushed one away

I had promised her that there would be no tears at her funeral and hastily brushed away one that had managed to escape.

The steam had all but cleared as I looked down at the white plastic stick in my trembling hands, my eyes eventually focusing on the pale blue line which had formed in the little window of the tube. I moved it back and forth, squinting in the fine mist, needing to be certain.

Just then, the bathroom door opened. Geoff stood leaning against the door jamb frowning, trying to make sense of the scene before him. I sat on the closed toilet seat, waving the device around wildly, and mumbling incoherently.

He saw the familiar white tube with its unfamiliar blue line and took me in his arms. Together we fell to the floor. I remember sobbing into the warm sleep scented hollow of his neck.

The world seemed to stop, frozen in time, as we knelt on the damp floor in stunned silence. In the background, the low, steady hum of the extractor fan continued in its

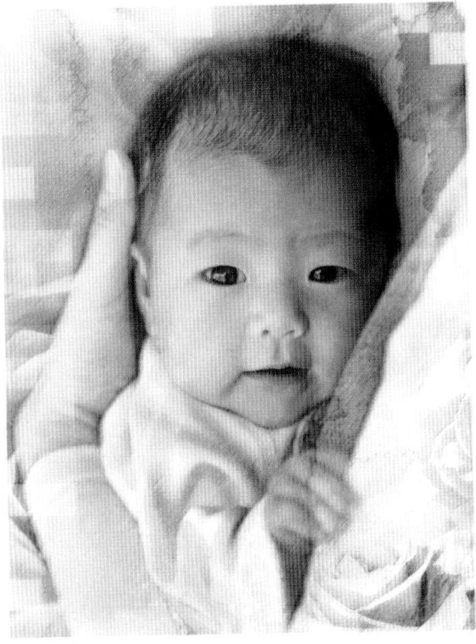

efforts to clear the remaining vapour that surrounded us.

After eighteen years of trying, four attempts at IVF, too much money and far too many tears, we were finally having a baby – naturally and completely without intervention.

Later that day, I stood by the open grave looking down at the rain soaked roses as they lay among the scattered dirt. The varnished surface of the coffin lid held tiny droplets of rain that slowly swelled as the relentless drizzle continued to fall. One by one they eventually burst and rolled down the side before disappearing into the cold sodden earth.

That's when it happened. I felt the brief touch of cold lips on mine. Caught her familiar scent on the damp afternoon breeze and as I turned to see who was there, I knew it was Mum, invisible but still somehow tangible.

She came home with me that day. When I was in the grip of morning sickness, she helped me to choose the arrowroot biscuits that would ease my nausea.

When raging hormones made me weepy and contrary, I know she chose the tunes that the DJ played on the radio and which cheered me up; and when I had my first scan and they couldn't find the heartbeat, I'm convinced it was she who gently turned my baby over to face the camera.

Lily is four months old now and has her father's smile, she occasionally chuckles to herself and I wonder if Mum is singing those bawdy nursery rhymes to her, that I couldn't understand but that still made me laugh so much.

She is still with us; on special days such as Lily's christening, and I know she will always visit, but I have to move on now and so does she. I can feel her slowly slipping away to her own destiny and I'm happy to let her go.

In the quiet moments when we nap together skin to skin, I look into my daughter's eyes and I see her grandmother and myself, and I know without doubt, that ghosts really do exist – if we allow them to.

Who Came Home?

They were very different people, but there was an instant and powerful connection between the woman and the islander

By Marian Hipwell

Her hair still glinted gold, as it had the first time Dan had seen her. He had been running trips for the holidaymakers from his small boat yard and she had been among the passengers. She had seemed out of place even then, like some exotic bird which had alighted by mistake on this damp island where the mist seemed to touch the tops of the hills and the beach was filled with fishermen, not sunbathers. Mostly middle aged people came to spend a few days here, not lovely women in their twenties and alone.

He had noticed her coming aboard but it wasn't until he heard her laugh at the antics of the seals in the ocean beyond the boat that he had turned and looked more closely at her. She had caught his glance and looked away after a moment. But he had known, even that early, that something more than a glance had passed between them. She had taken the next day's trip to the neighbouring island and the fishing trip the day after, shivering and hopeless with her line so that he'd had to help her. He had hardly dared to hope her reason for being there might have anything to do with him. That evening, he had found her in the small alcove which passed for a dining room at the island's solitary hotel.

"Hi again."

He had paused in front of her. If she had rebuffed him, that would have been the end of it, even before it had begun. But she had looked up at him and her eyes had widened with pleasure at seeing him. Her name was Fran Carter and she was a teacher, here for a month. They had spent every moment they could together, neither of them questioning how strange it was, he an islander who eked out a living with his boat and she a city dweller who would be going back to a world he knew little about. He had laughed when she told him she wanted to go and see Mairi. He couldn't remember a time when someone hadn't been wanting to go and see Mairi, called by some the island's

She had seemed out of place, like some exotic bird which had alighted by mistake

PICTURE: REX FEATURES ILLUSTRATION: JIM DEWAR

Continued overleaf...

He was mesmerised by the mysterious woman on his boat

Continued from previous page

wise woman, fortune teller, whatever. Others, including himself, called her eccentric and kept away.

"Where did you hear about her?" he asked.

"They were talking about her in the hotel last night." She had taken his hand. "Let's go. She might tell us if – if there's a future for us."

In the end they had gone, he standing near the door, skeptical and unsmiling, she seated across from the old woman.

Taking Fran's hand, Mairi had said, "I see one of you on a boat, while the other watches weeping from the shore. But dry your tears, because the one will come back."

The words irritated Dan. "What a load of rubbish." He had spoken curtly when they left. "Anyone would know you're a visitor and that you'll be leaving soon."

"But she said I'd come back." Fran touched his arm. "I will come back!"

He couldn't let himself believe her. Yet he still hoped as she sailed away; still watched and waited as summer turned into autumn. Only when winter settled its thick freezing blanket on the island had he stopped waiting. A letter arrived from her, telling him of her mother's illness and the need to stay with her. He would have gone to her then instead, but she hadn't asked. After a while he found he couldn't recall Fran's face. That had frightened him. If her image faded so easily, how soon before love did?

He had put to sea then, grieving in the only way he knew how, alone with the seals and the echo of her laughter in the cries of the wild birds. The weather changed with a suddenness he had never known. In later years, people would recall the freak storm which had come out of nowhere, taking even the weathermen by surprise. He had turned for shore immediately, yet the sea, responding to the mood of the skies, took the boat and tossed it at will. Grimly he hung on as the boat shuddered and strained. By some miracle, it stayed upright. Somehow, he managed to bring it into harbour hours later, knowing how near he had come to death. He had looked up then to see her watching by the jetty, her face tear-streaked and pale from the agony of the wait. She no longer looked like an exotic bird but a part of the island, as she stood among the others. Her hair still glinted gold the way he remembered and he knew he would never need to look for her face again in the sea.

After a while he found he couldn't recall Fran's face. That had frightened him

Unknowingly, on his way out, he had passed the ferry bringing her to him. He never thought until now that she, not he, would be the one watching, weeping on the shore. And that he would be the one to come back.

THE AUTHOR SAYS...

"They say life – and love – is all down to chance. But for some of us, there are times when chance needs just a little nudge from fate."

Brain BOOSTERS

Kriss Kross

Try to fit all the listed words back into the grid.

3 letters
Ado
Elf
Eve
Fob
Hue
Ice
Kit
Lab
Nod
Tug

4 letters
Anti
Beep
Chin
Diet
Eden
Fife
Hank
Tame

5 letters
Carer
Indie
Musty
Pinny
Scarf
Ulcer

6 letters
Bidder
Mouthy
Rebuff
Socket
Veneer
Yeoman

7 letters
Albumen
Elegiac
Flunkey
Inhuman
Stretch
Tenancy
Viceroy
Yardage

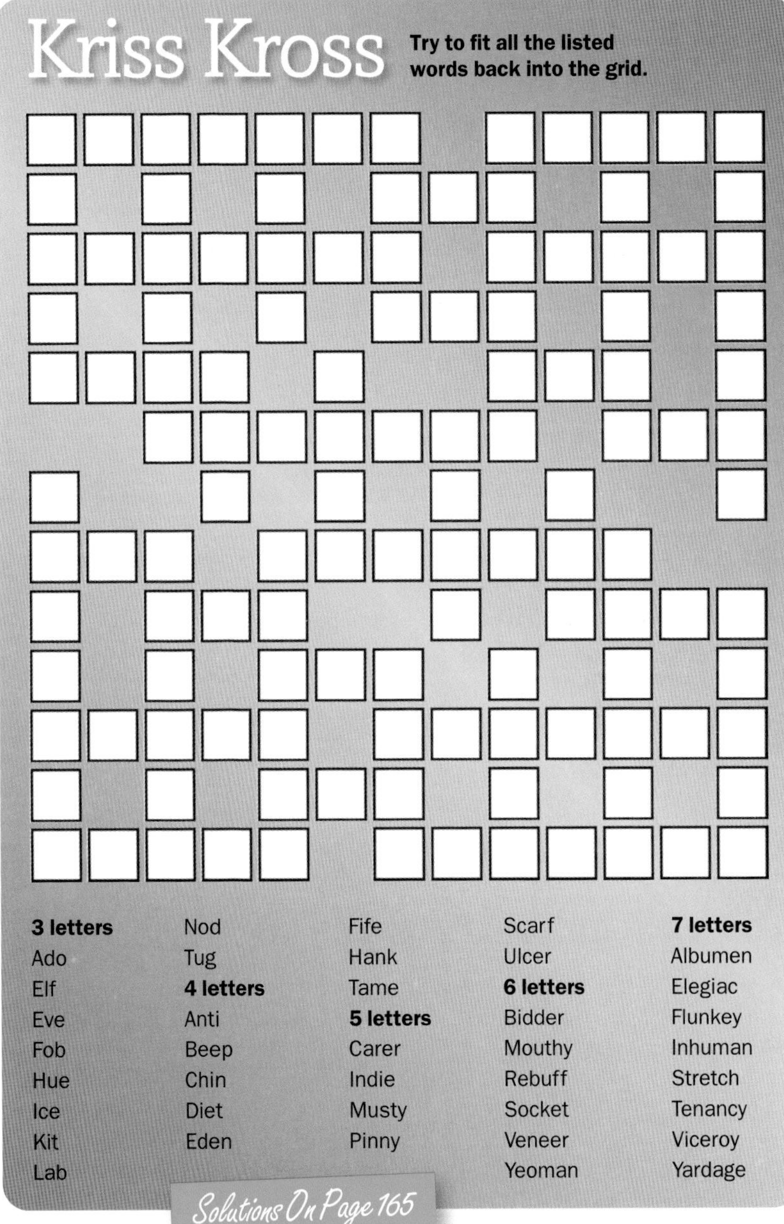

Solutions On Page 165

The Ring Of Truth

Harry's caring attention felt comforting to Joyce, but what would her late husband Bernard make of it all?

By Jo Styles

*omehow moving in together had seemed the obvious thing to do,* Ann thought, staring across the hospital corridor at her husband, Will.

Both her mother and Will's dad had been alone. They'd both lived a long way away and they were both getting on a bit. Now the kids had moved on to university the house had felt horribly empty, so why not move Harry and Joyce in?

Will grunted out, "Silly old foo–"

"Will!" Ann snapped before he could finish his sentence.

"Well, he is."

Everything in the house had been fine to begin with. Then on Wednesday Harry had fallen from a chair while trying to realign the curtain swags in Joyce's room. On Thursday he'd banged his head trying to adjust the lamp over her bed.

Now he was getting some stitches after cutting his head open trying to fix the shower in her en-suite.

Harry, it appeared, had developed an enormous crush on Joyce.

Joyce sat trying to twirl her wedding and engagement rings around and around her finger.

She certainly hadn't encouraged Harry's gallantry. In fact, lately, she seemed almost to be avoiding him.

Poor Mum. She just wants him to stop making a fool of himself, Ann thought. *He's making us all feel uncomfortable – especially Will.*

Joyce leapt to her feet as a nurse shepherded Harry along the corridor towards them. He had a big white lump of gauze taped to his forehead.

"I'm alright," he said, as Will heaved out an irritated sigh. "It's just a scratch. I'm sorry about dragging everybody out."

He likely thought it a victory that Joyce had decided to tag along at all. She'd had a visit to the Bingo planned and he hadn't been invited. Harry had smacked his temple against the showerhead on purpose, Ann thought, just to prevent her

Joyce certainly hadn't encouraged Harry's gallantry. Quite the reverse...

Continued overleaf...

PICTURES: THINKSTOCK ILLUSTRATIONS: JIM DEWAR

Harry liked to look after Joyce

Continued from previous page

from two-timing him with two fat ducks and a Bingo pen.

Joyce's brows creased. "That's perfectly fine, Harry," she said, sounding like a stern headmistress.

If he's ready to date then Harry needs to play the field, Ann decided, as they headed for the exit. *My poor Mum doesn't know what to do with him.*

"You want to do what?" Will asked the next day as Ann sat at the kitchen table making a list of nibbles and drinks.

"I want to have a party for Harry and Joyce, just a little get-together. I mean Harry did keep pretty much to himself when he lost your mum, while my mum, well, she went completely the other way when she lost my dad. I just thought if we let Harry mingle with Joyce's lady friends then… then…"

"…he might stop making an idiot of himself with Joyce?" Will suggested, just as a loud crash came from upstairs.

"It's alright," came Harry's yell. "It's nothing that can't be replaced."

"Like a hip or a knee," Will muttered darkly. "A party it is then," he said to Ann. "And the sooner the better."

Men proved to be a little thin on the ground at the party that weekend. In fact, in Joyce's age group they seemed like gold dust. Joyce had managed to round up only two to keep her fifteen Bingo friends amused. One of the elderly gentlemen took control of the music, another volunteered himself for the job of refilling everyone's glass, which left Harry in charge of the dancing. He bopped about like a penguin in the snow one second, did a very energetic jive the next, then decided a waltz was in order. Each dance collected up a completely different partner.

"He looks like a kid in a sweet shop," Will murmured into Ann's ear as they handed round nibbles.

Meanwhile Joyce sat primly in a chair in the corner, trying to twist her rings around and around.

"Are you having fun, Mum?" Ann asked over Frank Sinatra warbling out *My Way.*

"Oh yes," Joyce said while looking like she had a wasp caught in her mouth. "I just need… need some fresh air." Off she went looking like a scolded whippet.

Were those two pensioners smooching in her hall, Ann wondered, as she passed

"A party it is then… and the sooner the better," Will muttered to Ann

a couple in a huddle on her way through to the kitchen.

She was about to push the door open when she heard her mum speaking.

"I know you don't want me to take off my rings, Bernard. I'm not sure I want to either really..."

Ann hesitated. Bernard was her dad. Was her mum talking to his ghost in there?

"I know you're trying to send me some kind of sign, I just do," her mum added.

Ann hurried in, half expecting to be confronted by a ghostly apparition, but no, no ghosts, at least none she could see.

"Isn't the party going well, Mum?" she said innocently as her mother thrust one hand behind her back. Ann made herself busy, arranging sausage rolls on a plate while her mother looked contrite. "Harry seems to be having a lovely time. The ladies are queuing up to dance with him."

Joyce blanched. "He better watch out for that Margaret Rogers. She has hands like an octopus."

Ann frowned. "You're not jealous, are you, Mum?"

Joyce shook her head a little too quickly. "Of course not, and it wouldn't matter if I was. Your dad won't let me go."

"He won't what?" Ann frowned as her mother held out the hand she'd been hiding. Was that butter smeared all over her diamond engagement ring and gold wedding band?

"I'm sure I haven't put on any weight," she said. "But my rings are just so tight. I told your dad they needed resizing but... but he won't let me take them off." Joyce's voice trembled.

So that's why her mum spent so long twirling her rings about – she'd been trying to take them off.

"Iced water," Ann said firmly. "That'll do it. Quick, let's go out into the garden where we won't be disturbed."

"Really, Mum, I'm sure if you did meet someone new Dad wouldn't mind," Ann said, ten minutes later as the pair of them sat at the patio table. "You know he'd just want you to be happy, don't you?"

"I know you don't want me to take off my rings. I'm not sure I want to either..."

"Do you think so?" Joyce replied doubtfully, ice cubes clinking against the sides of the bowl she had her reddening fingers dipped into. "I never even considered seeing anyone else after I lost him. I had plenty of friends and the Bingo. Only when I moved in here... and Harry..."

She gave a mournful sigh as she glanced to the house, clearly thinking of Harry inside it about to be snapped up by one of her many friends.

"Well, I knew he'd started thinking about me in a different way when he started falling over himself. Then I noticed he'd taken his wedding ring off. I asked him about it and he said it had just slipped off, no problem at all."

She plucked her hand from the icy depths and frowned at her own rings worriedly. "Maud was ready to let him move on, he said. He said he was going to buy a little gold chain so he could wear her ring close to his heart."

She blushed then gave a little start.

"He's never asked me out. I... I mean I'm not taking my rings off to encourage

Continued overleaf...

Continued from previous page

him… they're just so, so tight," she said with a sigh.

"Let's try again," Ann said, taking her mother's hand and giving her rings an experimental tug.

"Ah!" Joyce said.

"Your finger-joint does look a little swollen, Mum."

Ann gave the rings a sudden swift yank this time.

"Ouch!" Joyce shrieked. "Ann, that hurts." She pulled her hand away and nestled it to her chest. "It's hopeless. I've tried everything: butter, window cleaner, washing-up liquid. I'm telling you. It's a sign, an omen. Your dad never wants me to take them off."

The back door slammed and they both jumped. "So this is where you're hiding." It was Will. "They're crying out for sausage rolls in there, you know."

If her mother needed a sign, would she object if it came in the shape of pliers, or even a hacksaw, Ann wondered. She pulled Will out of earshot and explained the situation.

Will eyes grew as wide as saucers. "You want me to fetch what? Because she thinks, what?"

Will was about as romantic as a sledgehammer.

"Just go to the garage and see if you can find a few things that might help," Ann said giving him a shove across the garden.

Dad's just being silly, Mum. He knows you'll always love him with or without his rings on your finger," Ann said when Will returned carrying his huge metal toolkit. "I bet once he sees the hacksaw those rings will fly off, Mum, and if not… well, we can always get a jeweller to repair them."

"There must be something else we can try," Joyce insisted as Will pulled out a hacksaw and loomed over her.

"This won't hurt a bit, Joyce." He smirked. "You have far too many fingers anyway."

"What an earth's going on?" somebody boomed out behind them. They all looked round. There Harry stood looking confused.

Joyce shook her head. "It's nothing, Harry," she blustered. "Go back to the party and your… your lady friends."

"My what?" Harry said a little indignantly. "I don't have any lady friends. And there isn't any party without you, Joyce. You ought to know that."

Oh, Harry, Ann thought. *What a sweet thing to say.* She opened her mouth to explain what they were doing just as her mother grabbed hold of her hand.

"It's nothing, Harry. Go back to the party and your… your lady friends"

"Don't tell him," Joyce snapped, her eyes full of panic.

But if Harry can't persuade Dad to let you go, nobody can, Ann thought. *Considering how much he adores you.*

Yes, the man who fell off chairs, cut himself on showerheads and bumbled about like a love-sick schoolboy was sure to persuade Bernard that if Joyce needed a hero, he was just the right one.

As soon as he understood the problem Harry puffed out his chest. "I know what we need," he said. "I just need to fetch something from the bathroom."

Five minutes later, Harry sat knee-to-knee with Joyce, both their faces as pink as the roses in the garden.

"With this dental floss," Harry said softly as he gently wound a great length of it around and around the joint of Joyce's finger to flatten it down, "I thee temporarily un-wed."

He gazed upward into the scudding clouds. "With your blessing Bernard, of course." He looked into Joyce's eyes and Joyce, despite insisting that Harry meant nothing to her at all, looked deeply into his.

Ever so gently, with the help of the dental floss, he eased both rings from Joyce's finger.

Bernard had decided to release her at last.

Harry placed the rings into Joyce's palm and she curled her fingers about them. "I think we ought to go into town tomorrow to get them resized for you."

"I… I think I'd rather buy a gold chain so I can keep Bernard's rings close to my heart," Joyce said, sounding a little hoarse. "Just the way you keep Maud's close to yours."

By Ann's side Will turned white.

"Oh my–"

"Shhh," Ann hissed at her husband, yanking him across the garden to give their parents a little privacy. "Isn't it lovely?" she breathed. "She was falling for him all along."

Will's eyes widened. "It's not lovely at all. They'll be in our house."

"If everything works out, I'm sure they'll want a place of their own."

"Let's hope Joyce keeps the ambulance service on speed-dial." Will replied acidly.

Off inside Joyce and Harry went, hand in hand, suddenly looking like a couple of smitten teenagers.

Will frowned at them for a long second then he too gazed heavenwards. He looked at Ann then, his brows creased as he spoke as if he were shocked by his own soft words. "I do love you, you know. We've been together so long sometimes I… I just forget to say it."

"I… I love you too," Ann stammered. She searched the clouds herself. Maybe someone up there really was looking down on them.

Thank you for that, she thought with a smile. *Thank you for reminding me I have someone I'll always want to keep close to my heart too.*

THE AUTHOR SAYS…

"This was inspired by a friend of mine who after breaking her wrist had to have her wedding ring cut from her poor swelling finger. 'I hadn't cried up until then,' she said."

Teatime Treats

Just perfect for a birthday or for spoiling someone special

Cappuccino Cupcakes

Preparation time: 25min
Cooking time: 25min
Makes 12

Ingredients

- **150g sugar**
- **150g butter**
- **3 eggs**
- **100ml whipping cream**
- **1½tbsp instant coffee powder**
- **150g self-raising flour**
- **55g ground almonds**
- **1 pinch salt**

For the buttercream:

- **110g unsalted butter**
- **225g icing sugar**
- **1tsp vanilla extract**

To decorate:

- **Instant coffee powder**
- **12 roasted coffee beans**

1 Preheat the oven to 180°C, Fan Oven 160°C, Gas Mark 4. Place 12 paper cases in bun tins.

2 Beat the sugar and butter until creamy. Beat in the eggs and cream. Sift in the coffee and flour and stir into the egg mixture with the ground almonds and salt.

3 Spoon into the cases. Bake for 25min until risen and springy to the touch. Cool on a wire rack.

4 Buttercream: beat the butter until soft. Sift in the sugar, add the vanilla and beat until smooth. Pipe swirls on the cakes. Sprinkle with coffee powder and decorate with coffee beans.

RECIPES AND PHOTOGRAPHY: STOCKFOOD

QUICK AND EASY TO MAKE

Chocolate Marshmallow Cupcakes

Preparation time: 20min
Cooking time: 15min
Makes 12

Ingredients

- **150g butter**
- **300g caster sugar**
- **3 eggs, beaten**
- **250ml milk**
- **225g plain flour**
- **1 pinch salt**
- **1tsp bicarbonate of soda**
- **55g cocoa powder**

For the chocolate frosting:

- **150g butter**
- **160g icing sugar**
- **1tsp vanilla extract**
- **110g plain chocolate, 60% cocoa solids, melted**

To decorate:

- **110g plain chocolate, chopped**
- **110g walnuts, chopped**
- **Mini marshmallows**

1 Heat the oven to 180°C, Fan Oven 160°C, Gas Mark 4. Place paper cases in 12 bun tins.

2 Beat the butter and sugar until creamy. Beat in the eggs and milk. Sift in the dry ingredients, stirring well.

3 Spoon into the cases. Bake for 12-15min, until a skewer inserted into the centre comes out clean. Remove from the tin and cool on a wire rack.

4 For the frosting: whisk the butter and icing sugar until light. Whisk in the vanilla and melted chocolate, increase the speed and whisk until smooth and glossy.

5 Spread the frosting on the cupcakes. Decorate with chopped chocolate, walnuts and marshmallows.

The Only Girl For Me

That longed-for path you didn't take might not have been meant for you, but for someone else in your life instead…

By Elaine Chong

Smoke from the bonfire billowed up into the air. Soon a great, grey cloud hung over the garden. George had decided to wait until the wind dropped before he set light to it, but now he wished for a light breeze to carry the smoke away. It stubbornly refused to move and simply drifted back and forth across the allotments.

"Hey, George!" a voice called out from somewhere in the darkness.

George strained his eyes to see through the cloud of smoke, and then recognised Jake as he stepped into the light of the fire.

"What are you doing out here at this time of night?" Jake asked him.

"I'm burning stuff," said George.

"Isn't it a bit late for a bonfire?" the younger man suggested kindly. "You can't see what you're burning."

"I know what I'm burning," said George morosely.

They stood side by side, drinking and watching the bonfire burn itself down

He saw Jake cast his eyes over the pile of boxes and bags, which he had spent the afternoon moving from the house to the bottom of the garden with a wheelbarrow.

"What are you burning?" Jake said.

"Stuff I don't want," replied George gruffly.

Jake smiled. "Do you want a hand?" he offered. "There's no wind and the quicker you get this lot on there," he pointed to the boxes and bags, "the quicker the smoke'll be gone."

George handed him an ancient garden fork, now blackened and singed the length of its wooden handle, and told him to make sure that everything he put on the bonfire stayed on the bonfire. Then he began to throw the boxes and bags into the flames.

They worked on in silence for the next half hour, George throwing bag after bag into the middle of the fire and Jake using his fork to keep it turning and burning.

George's face was flushed from the

Continued overleaf…

Jake looked long and hard at the ring

Continued from previous page

heat of the flames. At eighty-four he was probably too old, he thought, to be hauling boxes about or building bonfires.

He watched Jake work and recognised a young man in his prime. Tall and strong and all his life before him, thought George a little wistfully.

Jake was concentrating on keeping the fire going but he suddenly looked up and caught George's eye.

"So, what's with the late-night bonfire?" he said and offered George an encouraging smile.

George just shrugged in reply.

The bonfire had gradually become a glowing bed of blackened, oddly-shaped objects. The cardboard boxes and plastic bags had quickly succumbed to the flames but their contents continued to blister and burn. Every now and then something would sizzle and sigh and tongues of yellow flame briefly flickered brightly and disappear again.

Jake disappeared for a while, leaving George alone in the darkness. When he returned he was carrying several cans of lager. He ripped back the ring-pull on one of the cans and offered it to George, who accepted it wordlessly.

They stood side by side drinking and watching the bonfire burn itself down.

"Thanks for this," George said at last, and saluted Jake with the empty can. "Burning stuff is thirsty work."

"It must have taken you quite a while to get all this out of the house and wheel it down here." Jake said.

George considered this for a moment. "Took a lot longer sorting it out and packing it up," he said, and threw the empty can into the fire.

"How long?"

"About twenty years."

"You took your time, then," said Jake.

"Well, time is something that I've got plenty of," he said. He looked up at Jake. "What about you? Why aren't you out with that girl of yours?"

Jake tossed his own empty can into the fire. "How do you know about Amy?" he said crossly. "Have you been talking to Gran? I know she thinks she's helping, but I don't need her minding my business."

George bristled visibly. He turned his back on Jake and began to kick over the glowing embers. They exploded into firework showers and then floated off into the darkness. Even the smoke was slowly beginning to drift away. He turned to walk back into the house, but Jake placed a tentative hand on his shoulder.

"I'm sorry, George," he said. "It's just that everyone keeps asking me about Amy and I hate having to explain about it over and over."

Even in the gloom George recognised the pain in the young man's face

"You don't have to explain anything to me, lad," George said.

Even in the gloom of the garden, he could recognise the pain in the young man's face. It was covered in a fine layer of black ash and suddenly, without warning, a single tear ran down his cheek leaving a pale trail. Embarrassed, he wiped it away with the back of his hand.

A swell of sympathetic emotion rose up in George's chest.

"I had a girl once," he said softly. "Her

Memories flooded back

name was Ruby and she was the most beautiful girl I'd ever seen."

"Amy's pretty special too," Jake said.

Just saying her name out loud brought the memories flooding back. Memories of a night much like this one, he thought, with the smell of wood smoke in the air and the garden bathed in moonlight.

Ruby was special; he knew that from the first day they met. He remembered her long black hair and brown eyes that sparkled with laughter. And he remembered her smile and her full, red lips. When she kissed him goodnight, he closed his eyes and every bad thing in his life was forgotten.

"I'm going to call you Gorgeous George," she told him and poked him playfully in the middle of his chest.

He grabbed hold of her hand. "Will you be my girl?" he asked her.

She laughed, but she didn't say no.

They went dancing on a Saturday night, and in his arms she moved with a sensual grace. She leaned into him and he felt her warm breath on his cheek as she tilted her head and brushed her lips against his mouth.

When he wasn't with her, he thought about her every waking moment. And when he was with her, nothing and no-one else existed.

"I want you to be mine forever," he told her. "I want you to marry me, Ruby."

"Marry you?" she said, and laughed. "Find me a fine ring for my finger then," she told him and pushed him away.

He had no money to buy her a ring, but he had a good watch and a best Sunday suit to leave with the pawnbroker. His parents had been scornful and angry when he told them what he'd done, but he didn't care.

It wasn't enough for a shiny, diamond solitaire, but in the window of the jeweller's shop he saw what he was looking for: mounted on a slim gold band

Continued overleaf

Continued overleaf...

was a flower set with gleaming, blood-red stones. It was both charming and exotic, and it reminded him of Ruby.

An early autumn chill had invaded the garden when he drew her outside that night. Shy, unsure of himself still, he simply handed her a small, white, silk-covered box containing the ring.

He watched her face intently as she opened it up.

"A ruby ring!" she exclaimed and her eyes shone with excitement and surprise.

"Not rubies," he told her gently. "Red garnets, but it's everything I have."

He took the ring from the box and reached for her hand to place it on her finger, but she closed it tightly into a fist and pulled away from him.

"Poor man's rubies," she said without looking up at him.

"I am a poor man, Ruby," he said, "but I feel like the richest man in the world when I'm with you."

He reached out for her again but she moved away from him, shaking her head.

"I won't marry you, George," she said. "You're a sweet boy, but I'm not the girl for you."

She turned and ran from the garden, leaving him with the ring and the box and a broken heart.

Jake bent down and picked up the garden fork from where he'd left it lying on the ground. He used it to turn over the ashes in the fire. It was still burning, but everything that George had thrown into the flames was gone forever.

"Amy wants to get married," he said, almost to himself.

"I think most folk do," said George.

He looked up into the night sky and let out a huge sigh of relief. The cloud of smoke had finally drifted away high up into the air, leaving only a tell-tale smell of burning.

Jake was still slowly stirring the fire. He said in a low voice, "Why didn't you get married, George?"

"There was only ever one girl for me," he replied quietly, "but it wasn't to be."

All around them the lights in the houses were gradually being switched off, one by one, till only the street lights and a single light in the house behind them still burned.

"It looks like everyone else has gone to bed except you and me," said Jake. He gave the fire a final stir and then handed the fork back to George. "Just tell me one thing," he said, "what were you doing out here tonight, burning all this stuff?"

"I could ask you the same question," replied George.

Jake laughed. "You're not going to tell me, are you?" he said.

George hesitated for a moment. "Tell you what – you tell me first why you won't marry your Amy."

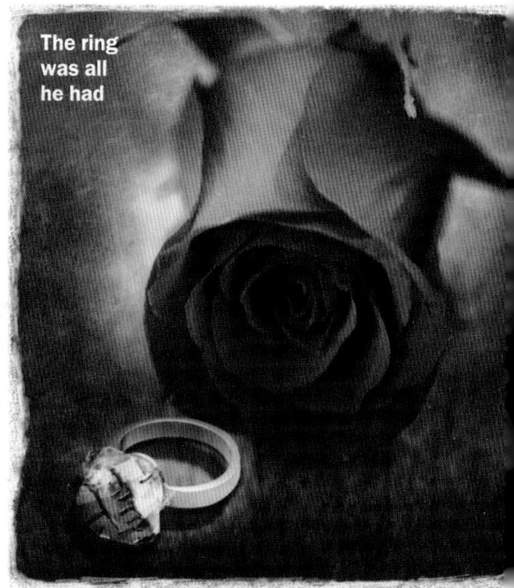

The ring was all he had

"That's easy," said Jake. "No money, so no future. I'm still living at home, and I can't even scrape a few pounds together to buy her a ring."

"Does she want a ring?" George asked.

"She says she doesn't, but how do you ask a girl to marry you when you can't even afford to put a ring on her finger? What kind of a promise is that?" he said.

Jake kicked at the ground with the toe of his worn boot.

"Now it's your turn," he told George.

"There's nothing much to tell," said George. "Me and your Gran grew up in this house. Of course, Rosy got married and moved out, but I've spent my whole life in this place. You can collect an awful lot of stuff in a whole lifetime that you don't really need and don't even really want any more."

"Have you actually got anything left?" Jake asked him.

George smiled. "A few bit and pieces," he said. Then he reached inside his jacket and pulled out a small, white box. "But you can have this, if you want."

Jake backed away. "I don't need paying, George," he said. "Trust me, it was good to talk to someone who's just happy to listen."

For several, long, uncomfortable seconds neither of them spoke or moved. Then George, fingers trembling, opened up the box. He drew out a slender, gold ring set with rich, ruby-red stones. With halting steps he walked over to where Jake stood next to the bonfire, grasped his warm, young hand, slipped the ring into it and closed his strong fingers around it.

"I had a girl once," George said softly, "and I wanted her to have this ring. It was everything I had, but it wasn't enough for her. You have it, lad – and be happy."

Jake uncurled his fingers and looked long and hard at the ring. "I can't take this," he said.

With trembling fingers he drew out a ring set with rich, ruby-red stones

George sighed. "You've noticed I'm not inclined to offer advice, especially when it's not wanted," he said, "but when you find a girl who loves you no matter who you are or what you've got, you hold on to her and you never let her go."

He turned to walk back into the house and then paused.

"It's been a lonely sort of life, and to tell you the truth, I'm right looking forward to you both moving in."

"I don't understand," Jake said.

"You and Amy," George answered with a warm smile. "Your Gran says I need looking after, so I've cleared out a few rooms." He reached up and drew a finger through the layer of soot on Jake's face. "You might want to take a bath before you go down on one knee, Jake lad. You look like you've been round a bonfire all night!"

THE AUTHOR SAYS...

"I wanted a ruby ring for my 18th birthday, many years ago now, but my parents couldn't afford one, so I chose a beautiful garnet ring like the one in this story. It's a cherished possession."

Bunny Girl

Behind the smiles, the posh pyjamas and flashing ears lay a completely different person – if only they all knew...

By Lydia Jones

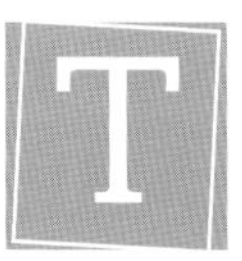

The bunny ears flash fluorescent pink. In front of me a queue has formed: women eager to part with money for this furry accessory. There are shrieks of laughter as they flick switches and begin shimmering.

Amanda would never have worn such a thing; too scared of looking silly. But Amanda was scared of lots of things.

"You in the queue, love?"

A cheery blonde in a dazzling white pyjama suit jerks her thumb at the line.

"Err – no."

"I'm Becky."

She smiles. A gold nose stud glitters under the spotlights.

"Not people-like-us," Amanda would have murmured, aghast. "We have nothing in common. Whatever would we talk about?"

"Who're you walking for, then?" Becky asks as if she's seen me every day for months, and hasn't just met me in my pyjamas at the local sports centre.

"Amanda."

"She a friend, was she?"

"Sort of."

"I'm walking for my Mum, me."

Becky pays; the vendor grins and passes over flashing pink fur.

"Not that you have to be doing the pyjama cancer walk for anybody." Becky clips on her ears. "I mean, it touches everyone, cancer."

"I've always been so careful," Amanda had protested when they told her.

Amanda was a woman without excess. Without vice. Unless you count shyness.

"Shall we go and sign the poster, then?" Becky asks me cheerily.

"Huh?" I look blank.

"It's over on the table. You write the name of the person you're walking for and a message. They're going to put it up so everybody can see."

Becky grins like this is the most amazing thing ever. I swallow a throat-rock at the thought of publicising something so personal.

I swallow a throat-rock at the thought of publicising something so personal

"Come on." She pulls my arm.

"OK." It's not as if anyone will know.

"Miss you, Mum," Becky writes, giving swirling tails to the Ms and drawing a circle over her 'i'."

There are lots of Mums on this poster... swirly ones, capital ones. All of them heartfelt and here for a reason.

Continued overleaf...

It's not as if anyone will know...

Continued from previous page

I give Amanda a tall, straight "A". It's funny but, written down, her name looks like her: tall, neat, evenly spaced.

Strangers often mistook her shyness for snobbery. It wasn't that she didn't want to talk to people; she just didn't know how. Communication was a hurdle. Even with Justin.

"He's lucky to have you," her friends always told her.

But she didn't believe it. Even on her wedding day she'd gazed trance-like at confetti thrown by smiling guests and felt that somehow there had been a mistake. Popular, centre-of-attention Justin couldn't possibly have chosen her.

And if you don't believe you're good enough, then eventually of course, you're not. Poor Amanda. When Justin left, I think in many ways it was a relief.

"Those are posh PJs – silk, are they?" Becky points at bell-shaped sleeves that still seem to swamp my arms.

"I treated myself."

"You did right, love. Better make sure you don't split your pants in the warm-up aerobics, though."

She cackles and it's such a warm, full-throated sound I find myself laughing too.

Sedate spot-jogging gives way to star jumps and something the leotard-clad instructor calls "hip rolls".

"Just a thrust for cancer," she trills as we all emulate suggestive swaying.

Becky and I join hands. I feel young and silly and oddly free.

"Off you go, girls," the instructor bellows. As one, we all snap our glow-sticks and set off.

"Go on – you know you want to," Becky urges mischievously as we pass the bunny ears stall.

I giggle, and suddenly I'm reaching for my money.

Amanda might never have worn them. But I am not Amanda any more.

I have stared into the eyes of the cancer beast and faced it down. I will never be scared of anything ever again. From now on I'm going to cherish every remaining moment; fill them with warmth and new experiences.

I giggle, and reach for my money. From now I'm going to cherish every moment

As we pass the line of male volunteer stewards, one waves his torch at me.

"Good luck, Mandy," Stuart shouts and I give him the thumbs-up.

"That your bloke, is it?" Becky asks.

I met Stuart at work, only weeks before my diagnosis.

I think about those months of "being there", of holding my hand and telling me I was beautiful even when I had no hair.

"Yes." I smile. "I suppose he is."

Then I switch on my bunny ears and join the sea of flashing pink heads snaking out onto the dark streets.

THE AUTHOR SAYS...

"I recently took part in a charity cancer walk much like this one with my daughter. It made me think about all the different stories behind the walkers."

PICTURES: REX FEATURES, THINKSTOCK ILLUSTRATION: MANDY DIXON

Fancy That!

Red facts that make you go "**Wow!**"

In Greece, Easter eggs are dyed red and the Greek expression "touch red" is said when two people say the same thing at the same time

Two "heritage routes" in London still use the original red Routemaster bus

◆ **In Jamaica, a popular slang term for one who is under the influence or drunk is "red".**

◆ Red is the first colour you lose sight of at twilight.

◆ **The longest wavelength of light is red.**

◆ Only 1% of the world's population has red hair – Scotland has the highest rate at 14% followed by the Irish at 10%.

◆ **Men wearing red are more attractive and sexually desirable to women.**

◆ Bees can't see the colour red, but they can see all other bright colours. Red flowers are pollinated by birds, butterflies and wind, rather than bees.

Feng shui recommends painting the front door of a home red to invite prosperity to the residents

Chinese brides wear red for good luck

◆ **Red does not make bulls angry – they are actually colour blind!**

◆ **Red carpet treatment: giving privileged treatment to an important person.**

Red is the highest arc of the rainbow

In Chinese culture red was associated with fire, south, and summer

◆ Our bodies react to the colour red as if we've seen a threat and are in danger.

WORDS: BABS BEATON PICTURES: ISTOCKPHOTO, THINKSTOCK

Scene Of The Crime

The police would never believe my amazing story... but what if Edna and I managed to obtain some proof?

By Theresa Delamere

verything was in sharply etched focus: a female nurse injecting adrenaline into the heart; the huge African doctor administering the defibrillator; the jerk of the chest, the ebb and flow beside the bed as they repeated the procedure on the young woman who lay there. Her head was heavily bandaged and she looked pale around her dark eyebrows, but still surprisingly pretty. I should die more often.

I didn't feel any alarm as I gazed down at myself from the ceiling of Nightingale Ward. I admired the quiet efficiency and determination of the staff. I was in good hands. It reminded me of scuba diving; that feeling of flying in slow motion. Bliss.

I glanced round to see how the other patients in the ward were handling it; it can't be nice thinking you could be next.

Then I saw it happen. A theft.

A male nurse slipped into the ward – unnoticed in the emergency – and went to the nearest bed by the door. Edna lay there, melted into the sheets. He pretended to take her pulse whilst sliding her wedding ring off her finger. No-one noticed. As he left, he glanced upwards looking directly at me; I saw his greenish brown eyes clearly above his face mask. He blinked and left. It had taken, what – fifteen seconds?

I began to feel quite agitated. He was getting away! My body started to shake; the nurse put a drip in my arm, then a jolt and oblivion.

I could hear low noises and sensed movement around the bed. I pulled my Velcroed eyelashes apart. A pair of green-brown eyes loomed down over me. It was him!

I clenched my left hand tightly; he wasn't going to take my engagement ring if I could help it.

"Rest," he soothed as he lifted up my left arm and took my pulse.

I wanted to stop him but drifted off, finally coming round a day later in

I glanced around at the other patients in the ward. Then I saw it happen: a theft

PICTURES: MASTERFILE, THINKSTOCK ILLUSTRATIONS: KIRK HOUSTON

We plotted like Miss Marple

intensive care. I looked at my hand and was relieved to see that my ring was still there. I didn't see the male nurse again.

I recovered quickly. I was told that I'd had an allergic reaction to the painkillers they'd given me for cutting my head open after the crash when the car brakes failed.

However, I was more interested in finding out whether Edna's ring had really been stolen. I couldn't ask the staff but luckily Janice, a volunteer bringing books round the wards, made it her business to know everything.

"Any news?" I asked her innocently.

Her eyes lit up.

"Well, maybe I shouldn't be saying, but there's a thief about – lots of jewellery gone. Oh, you're engaged!" she added, noticing my ring and having a good look. "It's so pretty, too – and pricey. You're lucky to still have it."

"Yes," I said. "Would you know if Edna in Nightingale Ward had anything stolen?"

She thought so, but was more interested in telling me that the police

Continued overleaf...

Continued from previous page

were wrong to interview the staff. To her mind, the thief was a visitor.

I knew exactly who it was, but who would believe me? A witness suffering from a head injury, who saw the event whilst having an out-of-body experience – imagine the fun a barrister would have with me if it ever got to court. Nor could I tell the police – unless I found the ring.

I decided to talk to Edna about it so, when I was well enough to be sent back to the ward, I strolled over to her bed.

Edna was seventy-seven and had fallen over on some black ice whilst crossing the road to go for a doctor's appointment. She was nibbling on a Rich Tea biscuit. She smiled at me.

"Hello, Kerry," she said. "You gave us such a fright. How are you?"

I've noticed it's typical of her generation to be more concerned for others than themselves. We got talking and tears welled up as she told me her wedding ring had been stolen.

"I hate it when I do this, but forty-two years is a long time. I feel like I've been bereaved again."

I took the plunge and decided to tell her everything I'd seen. She listened intently as I spoke low into her good ear.

"What do you think?" I asked when I'd finished. She gave me her empty cup.

"When you get to my age, dear, these near-death experiences seem more and more appealing. I believe you."

"No-one else will. We need proof."

We thought a bit before we both said, "Miss Marple!"

We were going undercover.

Fortunately Edna was long-sighted, otherwise we would have missed him hurrying out of the hospital side entrance, coat over his head. I glanced at her – pearls of rain dripping from the end of her nose matching my own – and nodded.

"This is it."

"Be careful, dear."

"Of course."

I set off sounding more confident than I felt. Edna couldn't come with me, unfortunately. It was far too slippery to risk her having another fall so I'd arranged to report back at her house afterwards.

I soon realised we didn't need to worry that he would see me following him, for it was one of those days where the rain fell in folds and everyone was keeping their heads down. I followed him into the bowels of the Northern Line and tried not to stare at him through the steam-filled carriage. It was a thrill when he got off at Tooting Bec station: he hadn't a clue I was behind him.

He walked rapidly up some side streets and turned into a maze of suburban roads with me in squelching pursuit. Trainers were not the most appropriate footwear. I'd worn them in case I had to run, either to catch him up or away if the situation turned ugly.

Eventually he walked into the reception area of a flat-roofed building. "Summerfield Nursing Home" declared

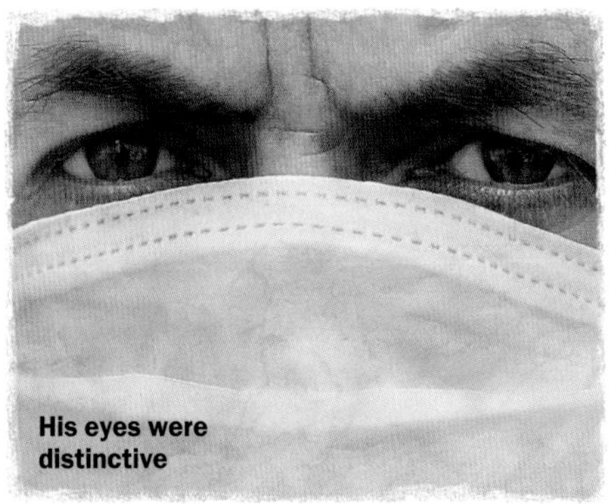

His eyes were distinctive

the graffitied sign outside. Looking at its dreary Colditz walls, I couldn't imagine a place less likely to remind me of summer. I felt very sorry for the people inside.

The receptionist saw me through the window. Her expression showed she thought I was mad or a prospective axe murderer, or both. I sloped off towards a shattered bus shelter.

I don't know how long I hung around there. The glamour of going undercover lost its attractiveness in direct proportion to the degree of frostbite I was experiencing in my fingers and toes. No way could I leave without him – I hadn't a clue how to get back to the tube station.

I was gazing at the multi-coloured hues of my nose in the remaining piece of cracked glass when I spotted him coming out of the building. I set off after him, relieved to be moving at last and feeling the agony of renewed life in my extremities as I did so.

The rain had finally eased into thick fists of iron-grey cloud resembling a pock-marked chin. We walked endlessly down repetitive streets until we finally joined the High Street, their twinkling lights a reminder of warmth. I thought he was going to buy food but he disappeared into a little shop next to the grocer's.

I crossed the road and stood in a doorway opposite. He had gone inside a jeweller's shop, but that was not what drew my attention. In its window was a large handwritten sign – *Pawn Broker.*

I moved out of my hideaway to get a better look. I could see him take something out of his pocket and put it on the counter. Some youths walked past me at that moment, and when I could take up my vantage point again he had gone.

Oh well. I'd just have to find out what he had pawned. I hurried across the road.

The clang of the door alerted the jeweller. It was very hot inside, thick with the heavy smell of bottled gas. I took down my hood and dripped over his lino.

"What do you want, love?" asked the balding man barely taller than the desk.

"No need to be bashful, love. The geezer before you sold his mum's wedding ring"

I realised I hadn't planned what to say.

"It's so nice to get warm, what a day!" I stalled, giving him my best smile while racking my brains.

Unwittingly he helped me out.

"Need to pawn a ring?" He indicated my engagement ring.

"Maybe," I said, instinctively hiding it with my other hand.

"No need to be bashful, love. The geezer before you has just sold his mum's wedding ring; happens to the best of us, especially with this flipping government."

I succeeded in persuading him to show it to me. It was a narrow, simple, eighteen-carat gold band with a white gold trim, very unusual. I knew it was Edna's; she had described it to me in detail.

Finally I managed to trade it for my engagement ring. I hoped Mick would understand.

Edna was a bundle of mixed emotions when I arrived coughing and spluttering on her doorstep. She was so thrilled to have her ring back, but concerned for me. She made me have a hot bath while she

Continued overleaf...

Continued from previous page

made some lentil and bacon soup and put my clothes in the dryer.

She was also rather feisty. She wanted to tackle him at the hospital. I thought it too risky, and said we should inform the police. Eventually I talked her round.

The next day we entered the blue-tiled Victorian walls of the police station. The charge sergeant checked their records on stolen property and verified that the ring was Edna's. He sent an officer to the pawnbroker's and the owner told him the ring had been pawned by a Jeffery James, an auxiliary nurse. They brought him in for questioning.

I sat in the station with Edna, sipping coffee and watching various drink-drivers and petty criminals being brought in. There was plenty of shouting which didn't seem to faze Edna at all.

My thoughts were on our own case. I had made a brief statement, and was concerned that someone would spot the flaws in it and ask how I'd known it was him. There was also something else I wanted to know.

When a policewoman called us over, I blurted out, "Why did he go to Summerfield Nursing Home?"

She explained his story; he had confessed to stealing jewellery in order to pay for his mother's care in the home. They had checked with his bank and it was obvious he wouldn't be able to afford the costs from his salary alone.

"Do you want to press charges, Edna?" she asked.

Edna looked at me inquiringly. I nodded. Mercy is greater than judgement.

"No, dear," she said and stood up. At that moment Jeffery James appeared from one of the rooms. He stopped when he saw us – he clearly recognised Edna.

"How did you know it was me?" he asked. "You were fast asleep."

"She saw you," said Edna before I could stop her.

"No-one saw me; they were too busy with the patient." His voice trailed off. "Was that you in the bed?" he asked me.

"Yes."

"Justice works in mysterious ways," said Edna. "Just be grateful I'm not pressing charges." She took my arm.

I could see him trying to work it out, and failing.

"Thanks," he mumbled before being led off for questioning. I hoped he would allow the other people to recover their jewellery, and that they would be as forgiving in the circumstances.

"Come on," said Edna, taking my arm. "I want to go and buy back your engagement ring from that pawn shop before Mick finds out."

"Do you want to press charges?" Edna was asked. She looked at me inquiringly

THE AUTHOR SAYS...

"Someone told me they'd had an out-of-body experience whilst in hospital for a head injury. It intrigued me. What if you saw a crime being committed in those circumstances?"

Fancy That!

Green facts that make you go "**Wow!**"

Green tea retains more antioxidants than black during the drying process, making it a popular healthy drink

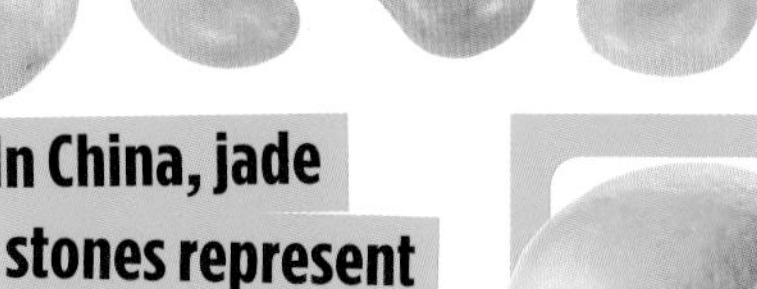

In China, jade stones represent virtue and beauty

◆ **Greener pastures: something newer or better.**

◆ The green kiwi is packed with more vitamin C than an equivalent amount of orange.

There are two main types of limes – regular green limes, or Persian limes, and the much smaller and more acidic Key lime

◆ Green is considered the colour of peace and ecology.

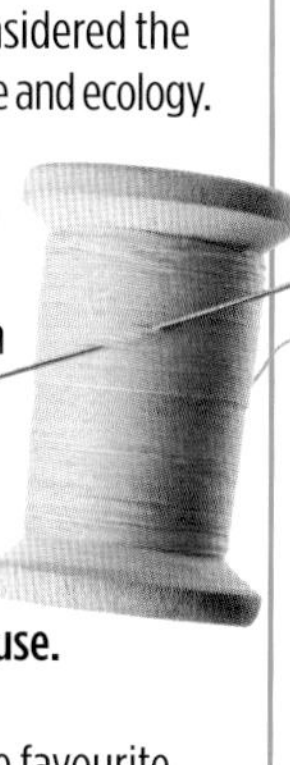

◆ **There is a superstition that sewing with green thread on the eve of a fashion show brings bad luck to the design house.**

◆ Green was the favourite colour of George Washington, the first President of the United States.

As the emblematic colour of Ireland, green represents the vast green hillsides, as well as Ireland's patron saint, St Patrick

◆ **In the Highlands of Scotland, people used to wear green as a mark of honour.**

Bright green is the colour of the astrological sign Cancer

Green leafy vegetables are among the densest sources of nutrition

◆ In Japan, green is regarded as the colour of eternal life.

Shadow Of Doubt

The painting stirred so many memories in me – but did I really want to re-live that uneasy time of my life?

By Linda Mitchelmore

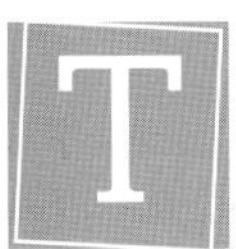

he drizzle had just begun to fall when I spotted the painting in the charity shop window; a simple painting, but perfectly executed, of a little girl wearing a sundress – halter neck, orange spots on a milky background. She had blonde hair in perfectly symmetrical bunches neatly tied with red ribbons, the bows standing stiff as rabbits' ears. Faded denim eyes and skin as flawless as alabaster. Childhood and summer captured in a wooden frame.

The little girl, in her leather sandals, was standing on an umbrella roundabout – its metal skeleton mole-black against an azure sky – in a park playground. She was reaching up, her hands clasped around an overhead strut and she was half-smiling at whoever painted the picture.

Just a painting, but it made best-forgotten memories bubble to the surface of my mind, in the same way gases rise, unbidden, from the bottom of a lake.

At the park, all Mum would let me do was stand on the umbrella roundabout

I'd had a dress like that – there was a photo of me wearing it in a pile of other photos I'd inherited from my mother.

I pressed my nose against the glass to see if I could see an artist's name. Yes, there it was, at the bottom of the left-hand corner, yet too far away still for me to make out the squiggly, indistinct writing from out here on the pavement.

It began to rain harder – fat drops that soaked the back of my neck in seconds, but my umbrella was in the hall at home.

It wouldn't hurt to get out of the rain, would it? To go inside the charity shop and read the artist's name?

The wind-chimes tinkled discordantly as I pushed open the door. There were no other customers, and the elderly woman reading a book spread open on the counter in front of her pulled her beige cardigan more tightly round her but didn't look up.

"That man's there again," I said. "He's looking at me, Mum."

Mum was sitting on a bench. I was so

Childhood and summer were captured in a wooden frame

longing for her to push me on the umbrella roundabout and feel the wind flutter my bunches, but she wouldn't. She never did.

Mum didn't like me getting my clothes dirty, or my knees scratched, or my hair messed up. So when we went to the playground in the park, all she would let me do was stand on the umbrella roundabout – lifting me up and then lifting me down again, as long as there were no other children with their mothers around. I was standing on it now.

I wondered why she took me to the playground every Saturday because all she did was sit on that bench, her legs crossed at the knee, sunglasses perched on top of her auburn curls, reading a fashion magazine – *Vogue*, usually.

"A man?" she said. "Where?"

"Over there."

Continued overleaf...

Continued from previous page

I pointed to where a man wearing dark grey slacks and a tweedy jacket lounged against the wooden fence. He had blond hair that reached past his ears and a fringe that flopped over his forehead, so you could hardly see his eyes, and he wore a shirt without a tie. My dad would never have gone out on Saturdays without a tie.

The man had a pencil in his hand and was sketching in a pad. I could see an open tin just crammed with more pencils on the ground by his feet.

"Do you think he's got double-ended crayons?" I asked.

I was dying to have double-ended coloured crayons. Bonita Cummings who lived two doors down from our Cornish unit flat at number 139 had a whole tin of them. From France. Crayon d'Ache. She said her grandma was French and had sent them from Paris.

"Don't be silly. That man's an artist. Double-ended crayons are for children. What would a man like that want with double-ended crayons?" Then she uncrossed her legs, pulled her sunglasses down from her tangle of hair and put them on. Then she stood up and smoothed down her skirt. "You can go round on the umbrella roundabout if you like."

"Can I?" I said. "And whizz it round? Really fast?" I thought I'd explode with excitement.

"Didn't I just say you could?" Mum returned. "But don't tell your dad."

Then she sashayed across the playground towards the man with the sketchpad and the pencils, a funny sort of smile on her face. I knew she didn't just mean to not tell Dad that she'd let me go on the umbrella roundabout, but that I wasn't to tell him she'd gone to talk to the man leaning against the fence either.

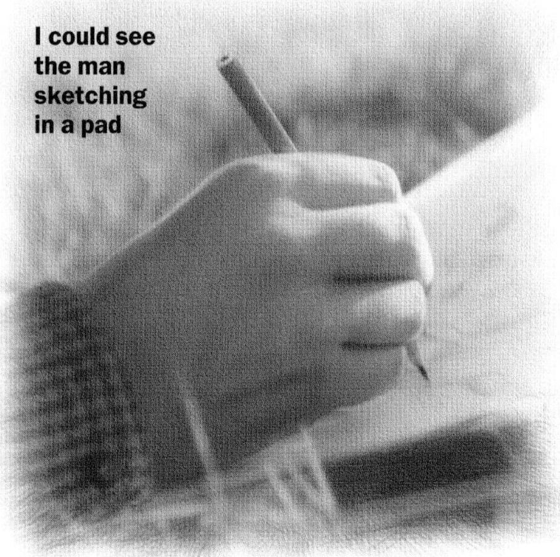

I could see the man sketching in a pad

The painting on display," I said. "Can I see it close up?"

The woman behind the counter looked up and sighed.

"It's only just gone in the window."

Well, I thought – where exactly does charity start? Was she committed to The Friends of Winner Hall or not? Perhaps this non-stop rain was getting to her, too. So I turned on my sweetest smile.

"I'll take it out carefully, then, and if I decide I don't want it, I'll put it back just as carefully."

"Alright, but I doubt it'll make your fortune."

"A fortune's not what I'm after," I said, and she gave me a funny look and went back to her book.

Up close, there was no doubt the little girl in the painting was the five-year-old me. The artist had even captured my broken front tooth. I had an instant flashback to the day I'd done that.

I'd been out with my dad at dusk, walking along, holding his hand, listening to him whistling – feeling safe. Dad worked for the council, mending roads and pavements and building walls. At dusk it was his job to light the lamps around the roadworks so cars and people didn't fall in and hurt themselves.

"You run on a little bit, lovey," he'd said. "I'm going to have a ciggie."

So, that's what I did and that's when I tripped on a jagged paving slab. I grazed both my knees, and cut my lip.

My forehead hurt where I'd banged it on the pavement. There was a lot of blood coming from my cut lip and when I put my hand in my mouth I found there was a bit of tooth missing.

"You clumsy clunk," Dad said. "You're not a bit like your brothers, are you?"

He picked me up and smoothed my hair and kissed my forehead. He rubbed my back gently with his free hand.

"No." I snivelled gratefully into the side of his warm, rough neck.

Dad was right – I wasn't a bit like my older brothers who were at the Grammar School, and clones of Dad with their black hair and bitter chocolate eyes. Able cricketers and athletes, both of them.

"There, there, don't cry. I do wonder where you came from sometimes. D'you think the fairies brought you?"

"I don't know," I wailed, and cried even harder.

Dad gave me a hug then, pulling me tightly to him – I could smell tobacco on his breath and Omo washing-powder on his overalls.

"Well, fairies or no, I love you just the same," he said, and his voice was all rough and gravelly.

He was a good dad, my dad and I loved him. I loved the way he always let me win at dominoes. I loved the way his hair became darker and glossier when he rubbed Brilliantine through it with his big, rough hands. I loved that he never got cross with me the way Mum did.

There was a lump in my throat because I couldn't remember the last time I told Dad I loved him – because I did. I might not have had his genes, but his love sustained me still. Time to give him a ring, invite him to lunch on Sunday.

I stared at the painting in my hands in The Friends of Winner Hall charity shop with only the sound of the rain outside and the occasional sigh of the woman behind the counter to break the silence. The painting seemed to speak to me, though, and I didn't know that I wanted to hear what it was saying.

I stood on the umbrella roundabout not knowing what to do now that I'd been given permission to ride on it.

I heard the man with the sketchpad and pencil say to Mum, "How's my girl?"

And Mum replied, "As you see her."

Then she giggled, but they lowered their voices after that and I couldn't hear what they were saying any more.

"I wonder where you came from sometimes. Did the fairies bring you?"

I stood there watching them – this man I'd seen watching me loads of times, and Mum. I saw Mum primp her hair. She took her powder compact with the little mirror in it from her bag and re-applied her lipstick.

She had hundreds of lipsticks in a drawer at home. Dad was always asking her if she wouldn't mind not spending quite so much of his hard-earned cash on

Continued overleaf...

Continued from previous page

lipsticks, but she didn't take any notice.

Then I saw the man put an arm around Mum's shoulders and she put her head against his neck. I knew only Dad was supposed to do that. So I leapt down off the umbrella roundabout and grabbed a railing and ran and ran, round and round, until my feet left the ground almost and I had to jump on. I was giddy with exhilaration and fearful of something I didn't understand.

I closed my eyes as I spun round and round, each turn getting slower and slower until it stopped and I opened my eyes again. He'd gone.

"Well," Mum said. "That's the last we'll see of him. David's going to Paris to live."

"In France?" I thought of Bonita Cummings and her French grandma. "Can you ask him to send me some double-ended crayons?"

"Don't be stupid," Mum said. "Why would David do that?"

I wondered how she knew his name.

"I'm closing in a minute," the woman said. She stood up, shut her book and slid it back onto a bookshelf, patting it neatly into place. She opened the till and began, very noisily, to count the cash and pour it from her palm into little plastic bags. "So, are you going to have that painting or not?"

"I'm still thinking about it," I said. I glanced at the clock. No need to rush – there were ten minutes to go before the shop officially closed, anyway.

I knew I ought to buy the painting because it was by David James Barclay. He's become very collectable these days. I knew the woman running this charity shop had no idea of its value – it was certainly worth far, far, more than the six pounds fifty she was asking for it.

I knew beyond any shadow of doubt that Dad had suspected something, that day when he said he wondered if the fairies had brought me.

Now, with the painting in my hands after all this time, I knew that my mother had been the artist's lover, but that she would never have been his wife. Because men like him do not do wives and families.

I knew beyond question that the man who had painted my picture was my father – but he wasn't my dad.

My dad was the man who brought me up, fed me, clothed me, helped me with my maths homework, held me tight when Joseph Todd broke my heart. My dad was the man who was the best grandad possible to my children.

So I put the painting back in the window and left.

The sound of the wind-chimes was melodic this time. Its sweet tones followed me all the way down Victoria Street.

And it had stopped raining.

THE AUTHOR SAYS...

"When I was about five years old, a man came up to my mother in a café and asked her whether he might draw me. I often wondered what happened to that drawing."

PICTURES: SUPERSTOCK, THINKSTOCK ILLUSTRATIONS: KIRK HOUSTON

Brain BOOSTERS

Missing Link

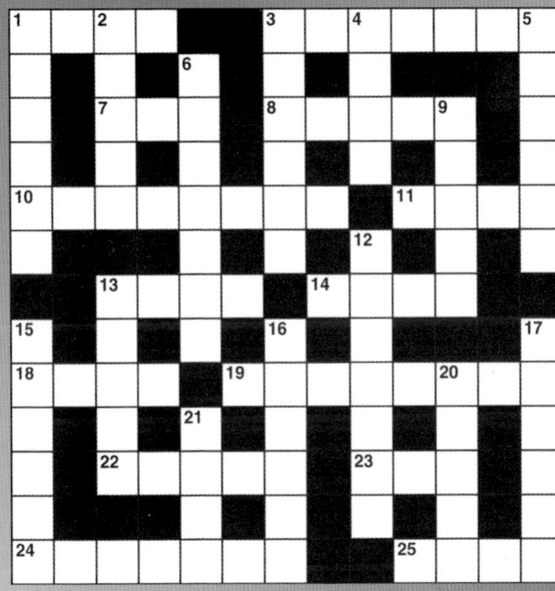

The answer to each clue is a word which has a link with each of the three words listed. This word may come at the end (eg HEAD linked with BEACH, BIG, HAMMER), at the beginning (eg BLACK linked with BEAUTY, BOARD and JACK) or a mixture of the two (eg STONE linked with HAIL, LIME and WALL).

ACROSS

1. Shell, Shelter, Stink (4)
3. Grand, Old, School (7)
7. Jam, Night, Storage (3)
8. Financial, Hard, Tables (5)
10. Company, Film, Managing (8)
11. Board, Main, Set (4)
13. Bully, Burger, Roast (4)
14. Battle, Flag, Space (4)
18. Kitchen, Trust, Vanity (4)
19. Common, Foreign, Hard (8)
22. Cocktail, Juice, Machine (5)
23. Craft, Hot, Pressure (3)
24. Finger, Hair, Happy (7)
25. Park, Roe, Stalker (4)

DOWN

1. Ash, Bottle, Strawberry (6)
2. Event, General, Sergeant (5)
3. Perpetual, Sickness, Slow (6)
4. Circle, Precious, Quaver (4)
5. Bag, Side, Sore (6)
6. Age, Price, Tax (7)
9. Album, Duty, Rubber (5)
12. Imaging, Springs, Underwear (7)
13. Case, Encounter, Moment (5)
15. Point, Proof, Rubber (6)
16. Cost, Leaf, Wood (6)
17. Bed, Catcher, Shell (6)
20. Centre, Gas, Optic (5)
21. Jury, Over, Parliament (4)

Solutions On Page 165

As Those Petals Fall...

When beleaguered Alison learns to depend on her own inner strength, she finds she can cope with anything

By Karen Byrom

e Loves Me Not... Alison stood at the kitchen window, gazing unseeingly into the garden that she normally tended with so much joy. Spring had come early this year, and gay daffodils vied with colourful crocuses, while against the wall, pink flowering currant bushes and vibrant yellow forsythia competed for the title of seasonal showstopper.

Indoors, hands that should have been digging in the rich dark earth, pulling out young weeds and tending small seedlings, instead shredded nervously at the petals of one of the shop-bought chrysanthemums waiting to be put in the vase Alison had pulled out from under the sink.

Shop bought? Garage bought, more like! Alison blinked away angry tears as she looked down at the flower she'd destroyed, hating its artificial brightness as well as all that it stood for.

Never, in all their years of marriage, through good times and bad, had Jack forgotten their anniversary. It was yet another symptom of the cracks that had been appearing over the last few months.

She'd tried to shield herself from her husband's silences, his increasingly long absences spent "working overtime" and his furtive phone calls that stopped the moment she appeared, by telling herself that he was under pressure at work, that he was having a difficult time facing up to middle-age, that he was missing his mother, who'd died suddenly last year. That his seeming indifference to her was just her imagination...

Yet thrust into her hands with little ceremony late yesterday evening, when he'd finally come home after phoning from the office to say not to hold back dinner for him as he was working late again, these flowers were the final straw.

She told herself that she had to face it; her husband must be having an affair

She'd dumped them in the sink, not even able to say thank you, while he disappeared upstairs to a hot bath and bed. By the time she'd pulled herself together and entered the bedroom, he was snoring gently – and when she woke this morning, he'd already left for work.

She told herself that she had to face it. He must be having an affair.

Continued overleaf...

PICTURES: THINKSTOCK ILLUSTRATIONS: JIM DEWAR

Continued from previous page

He Loves Me...

Fifteen-year-old Alison sat on the grass by the side of the school football pitch, gossiping and giggling with her friend as they plucked daisies from the ground and ruthlessly tore off their tiny petals.

"He loves me!" Alison declared triumphantly, waving the denuded daisy at Emma as she glanced sidelong at Jack, the devastatingly handsome and athletic sixth former currently chasing the ball up the football pitch.

"Cheat!" Emma shrieked. "You pulled the last two petals off together."

"Did not!" Alison denied, but her too-pink cheeks and sparkling eyes gave her away. She reached for the daisy Emma was holding. "Too late! I've won!"

The pair collapsed on the grass in a mock tussle, the noise finally drawing Jack's attention to his adoring fan club.

He grinned shyly as he drove the ball towards the goal and was rewarded by cheers from the girls.

Though it was another few weeks before Jack asked Alison out, they were a steady item for all of the following year. Then Jack left for university...

He Loves Me Not...

Looking back, Alison did not know how she got through the next three years without Jack. Theirs was a small town and she usually bumped into him on his infrequent trips home, but they were no longer going out together and, as often as not, he had another girl on his arm; one glamorous, grown-up student after another with whom Alison couldn't compete.

"Plenty more fish in the sea," Alison's mum said cheerfully, while her friend Emma coaxed her to "come out with the crowd on Friday".

Sometimes Alison did – she even dated other boys, but Jack remained her first love, and to him her heart was true.

He Loves Me...

Then Jack came home to take up a job at a local accountancy office and found Alison all grown-up and working at her dad's small market garden centre.

Suddenly he developed a keen interest in gardening, popping in at least three times a week to pick up "things for my mother" and staying to talk to Alison for far longer than was necessary.

Of course, she wasn't such a fool as to fall straight into his arms. With the thoughtlessness of youth, Jack had left her broken-hearted once – this time round, he'd have to woo her.

Which he did, with patience and flowers – delicate freesias from the local flower shop in spring, then bright roses from his mum's garden and, as summer drew to a close, asters pinched from the local park, to the amusement of the stern "parkie", who hid his romantic heart well.

Soon they were going steady once more.

There were red roses on Valentine's Day, colourful carnations on her birthday… and then, one magical day two years later, sweet baby's breath and delicate lily of the valley formed her bridal bouquet as she and Jack were joined as one in the sight of their fond families.

He Loves Me Not…

Lilies were the one flower Alison could not have in the house, and not just for their overpowering scent. Their pristine whiteness and cloying smell had the power to transport her instantly back to the darkest days she'd ever known.

Just two short years after their marriage, Alison and Jack stood side by side but not touching as the same minister who had presided over their union said prayers for the dead over the body of their little daughter, born too soon and too frail to stay in this world for more than just a few heartbreakingly short hours.

The newly-bereaved young parents could find no comfort in each other; instead, each folded up in their own sadness and the silence between them grew, until one day Alison could bear it no more and told Jack that she thought they should separate.

"If that's what you want," he said sadly.

But that night he appeared back home, bearing a huge bouquet of sweet-smelling flowers and asking her to reconsider.

"We've lost so much, Alison." He cried in her arms as she gently cradled his head. "Let's not lose each other, too."

As they talked deep into the night, she realised that she was at fault, too – that she had pushed him away instead of letting him comfort her.

By morning, their grief was still there but bearable, as they planned for the future.

The newly bereaved young parents could find no comfort in each other

He Loves Me…

There were flowers when their son was born a year later, bouquet upon bouquet as though the young husband couldn't thank his sweet wife enough for giving him not just a longed-for baby, but the chance to begin again. Two more daughters followed – none replacing their precious Jennifer, but each bringing joy in their own right.

Peter, Joy and Avril – all in their twenties now, and scattered around the country, but always in touch, never forgetting Mum or Dad at Christmas and birthdays, and coming together to plan a glorious silver wedding surprise party four years ago.

He Loves Me Not…

Would there be a thirtieth wedding anniversary? Alison wondered. Angrily she jammed the distasteful chrysanthemums

Continued overleaf…

Continued from previous page

into her least favourite vase – a show of defiance that only she would know or care about. Or would she instead be breaking the news of their father's infidelity to her children who, grown-up as they were, would be stricken at their parents' separation and torn between loyalty to their betrayed mum and guilty love for their even guiltier dad?

No! Alison slammed the vase down so hard on the kitchen counter that water splashed out over the floor. The cat, which had been snoozing by the radiator, shot up and away with an astonished meow.

She wouldn't let this happen to her marriage. She didn't know who her enemy was, but she'd fight her tooth and nail. After all, hadn't she sworn when she was nineteen, and Jack had come back into her life, that she would never let him go again?

They'd coped with life's greatest tragedy by talking, but what could she say this time that wouldn't sound accusatory and sad? *Is there someone else? Are you having an affair? Have you stopped loving me?*

Where would she find the strength to cope with his answers – whatever they might be?

With grim determination, Alison went to hunt for her gardening gloves.

He Loves Me?

It took time and patience, of course. Important things always do. Alison had learned that as a fifteen-year-old, waiting patiently by the sidelines to attract the attention of the school heart-throb.

She'd learned it in the years he'd been absent at Oxford, when she had done her own growing up. She'd learned it in the months following his return when she'd longed to throw herself into his arms and instead kept him at a distance so that he wouldn't risk losing her again.

So now, instead of moping and crying and hurling angry words, she got on with her life. She caught up with her friends and took up a long-standing offer to work several hours a week at the local flower shop, living life's ups and downs through the stream of customers who gratefully accepted the beautiful arrangements she offered up with a smile.

At home she kissed Jack goodbye in the morning and greeted him with a smile at night, no matter how late he came home. She cooked him his favourite meals – but wasn't always there to serve them to him.

Now it was his turn to ask where she'd been, to look at her, quizzically at first, and then with growing concern as he seemed to realise that perhaps, just perhaps, he was once more in danger of losing her…

There, in the small flowerbed she'd dug in the lawn, was a bright golden sun

He began coming home earlier. There were no more weekend conferences at work. His phone lay where he laid it down, available for Alison to look at his call history if she cared to.

She didn't bother. Of course she cared, but she was determined to trust in her own strength of purpose, rather than test his. She, of all people, knew Jack's frailties – hadn't they been married for almost thirty years? The good news for him was that she still loved him, despite all.

Their thirtieth wedding anniversary was celebrated with a quiet meal for two. Alison wasn't ready to pin too much hope on Jack's new attentiveness yet. But in the vase that graced their dining-room table was a flower arrangement to rival the loveliest she herself had ever put together herself, delivered from the most expensive florists in town, with a handwritten card of love and promise.

He Loves Me!

So the seasons rolled by and spring came round again. The daffodils and crocuses were in bud – but it wasn't until an unseasonally warm March day that they burst into bloom, overnight and all at once, it seemed.

Looking out of the bedroom window, at last Alison saw the fruits of last year's labour.

There, in the small flowerbed she'd dug out in the middle of the lawn – the one Jack had laughingly grumbled at as he mowed the grass each week over summer – was a bright golden sun, its centre deep and golden, its rays picked out in lighter yellows and whites.

The daffodil bulbs she'd planted a year ago had done their work, reminding her that there was a golden future ahead for her – with or without Jack.

She'd vowed that day last spring that he might break her heart but never her spirit. That even if she lost the fight, she'd win the war. That she would remember, no matter how great her pain, that spring was always around the corner.

An arm snaked comfortingly around her shoulder.

"It's like a new beginning," Jack's voice whispered in her ear. "Alison, did you… ?"

She turned and laid her finger against his lips. "It's a new beginning. For both of us – if you want it. If not, I'll do it alone." Her chin lifted proudly.

"Of course, I want it." His voice was suddenly fierce as he pulled her to him, holding her as if he would never let her go. "Alison, I'm so sorry…"

"Let's talk about it later," she said softly, relishing the warmth of her husband's embrace.

"But it's third time lucky, Jack. There are no more chances, you know."

"I swear I'll never let you down again," he said, his voice breaking.

For now, there were no more words. Just a blaze of passion to equal the blaze of golden daffodils that danced their happy promise in the sun.

THE AUTHOR SAYS…

"I always think daffodils are a sign of hope, flowering as they do after the dark days of winter. Here they symbolise Alison's hope and her faith that there will be sunshine after the darkness."

Made For Each Other

How was I to know what the repercussions would be as I tried to cheer up my poor, distraught childhood friend?

By Teresa Ashby

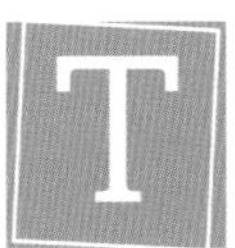

he minute I found Jenny's message in my voicemail, I told them at work I had a family crisis to deal with. Jenny's not strictly family, but we've been best friends since we were at pre-school and she's the closest thing I've ever had to a sister.

We used to joke when we were kids that if I married her brother, Ian, we would be sisters – sort of. I should be so lucky. When I got back from university, Ian had gone off to live and work in New Zealand and my best friend was engaged to his best friend, Mark.

"It's me," Jenny's tearful voice said. "You'll never believe this, Cressida. It's about the wedding… Everything's changed. Call me!"

The poor girl sounded heartbroken and I could hear her sobbing as she hung up.

I could do better than call her. A shoulder to cry on and a hug, that's what Jenny needed.

I had no idea what could have gone wrong. Jenny and Mark were made for each other. Whatever it was, I was sure, could be smoothed over. Mark didn't have a roving eye, his middle names were Honest and Faithful and he adored Jenny.

I stopped on the way for flowers, cake and wine, but when I got to Jenny's she wasn't answering her doorbell.

Her car was parked outside and – bless her – Jenny doesn't even walk as far as the corner shop if she can help it so I knew she was at home.

I tried the front door, found it unlocked and let myself in.

"Jenny?" I called. "Where are you?"

I put the wine in the fridge, dumped the flowers in a vase and left the cake on the table.

I knew everything there was to know about painful break-ups, but I'd never been with anyone for as long as Jenny had been with Mark and my heart had never been truly broken.

I knew all about painful break-ups, even if my heart had never been truly broken

I gulped down the lump in my throat. Well… maybe once, but he hadn't even been a boyfriend, so it didn't count, did it?

I brushed away a tear – where on earth had that come from? What did I have to

Continued overleaf…

PICTURES: THINKSTOCK ILLUSTRATIONS: MANDY DIXON

"I'm here for you, Jenny"

Continued from previous page

cry about? I wasn't the one whose life was in tatters.

I went upstairs expecting to find Jenny face down on her bed sobbing her heart out, but I could hear the splash of water in the bathroom and smell the scent of bubble bath.

"Are you alright in there? It's me, Cressida!" I called out.

There was a splash as if she'd dropped the soap, then a strange little squeak.

"Uh-huh."

Poor Jenny – she sounded distraught, as if her throat was clogged with tears.

"I don't understand it, Dad," he'd said. "They've just… disappeared."

It got worse. Their Dad took Ian's computer to bits, checking his hard drive and motherboard and power supply and all the rest of it.

"We'll just have to reinstall everything," he said, scratching his head. "Don't worry. It'll only take a few hours."

"A few hours?" Ian muttered. "What about all my saved games?"

"You can start them from scratch," I suggested, trying to be helpful. "It'll be like having a whole load of new games."

"Remember that time we wiped your brother's computer hard drive"

"I've brought wine and cake round, but you have a nice long soak and we'll drown our sorrows with sugar and alcohol when you come out."

I thought I heard a soft laugh. It was more likely a sob.

"Do you want to talk?"

She didn't answer.

I fetched a chair from the corner of the landing and sat down, my ear pressed up against the bathroom door.

"I'm here for you, Jenny," I declared. "I want you to know that. No matter what's happened, I'll always be here."

I thought she and Mark were rock solid. They were the happiest couple I knew.

"Hey, Jen – do you remember that time we borrowed your brother's computer to do our homework and accidentally wiped his hard drive?"

I hoped it would make her laugh, but she just groaned. Ian had never found out it was our fault. He'd spent ages trying to retrieve all his games.

I could still feel the chill from the look he gave me even now, all these years later. Still, at least he'd looked at me!

It was so unusual to see Ian without a smile on his face. He was always making us laugh, but when we wiped everything off his computer, he didn't smile for days.

I hoped recalling old memories would help take Jenny's mind off things. I chose memories from our early teens, before she started going out with Mark.

"What about the time we told Victoria Bradshaw that Ian had a pet frog called Herbert? Do you remember?"

I could hardly stop laughing. I hoped the memory would cheer Jenny up too.

"It was rotten of us, I suppose," I said, wiping away a tear. "But it would have been awful if he'd ended up going out with her, so we did him a favour really."

Not that he'd thought so.

"I just don't understand it," we heard him telling his mum. "She just broke up with me, muttered something about preferring her princes not to have frogs."

"Never mind, dear," his mum said soothingly. "These things happen."

He didn't smile for days then, either.

Jenny had gone very quiet in the bathroom.

"Are you okay?" I said.

"Mm-hmm."

She was too upset to speak and communicating through a series of strangled squeaks.

I knew something that would cheer her up.

"We weren't very good at choosing girlfriends for him, though. Remember when we told Amelia Taylor he fancied her? We didn't know she was already going out with Duncan Woods."

Poor Ian. He must have been terrified when Duncan and his mates went after him. I remember him sitting in his mum's kitchen afterwards clutching a cup of hot, sweet tea in his trembling hands.

"I managed to talk my way out of it," he said shakily. "But where on earth did Amelia get the idea I fancied her? She's not my sort at all."

He'd just seemed so hapless when it came to girls and we thought we'd help.

"Deep down I was glad he didn't end up going out with Amelia," I said. "I used to dream that he'd suddenly notice me, but of course he never did. I've always carried a torch for your brother, though you probably never noticed..."

I sighed. "Who am I kidding? Everyone knew about the crush I had on Ian – everyone except Ian!"

Hang on. It wasn't very tactful of me, was it, talking about past crushes when my best friend was in the middle of a terrible crisis? Change tack.

"What about that time he dressed up in your mum's clothes and pretended he was your dad's long-lost great aunt from Adelaide?"

Oh, a snort of laughter. Good! But who wouldn't laugh at the thought of tall, gangly Ian in a dress?

"Your dad's face! He was fooled until Ian started talking in that daft shrill Australian accent. He sounded like Dame Edna after she'd been breathing helium!"

Muffled giggles. Brilliant!

"So are you going to come out of the bath before you turn into a prune, Jen?" I called out. "Come downstairs and have a glass of wine and a piece of cake and we'll sort everything out together."

At that moment I heard a key in the front door. Leaping up, I peered downstairs

At that moment, I heard a key in the front door. I jumped to my feet and looked down the stairs – and saw Jenny and Mark coming in.

"*Jenny?*"

She looked up with a beaming smile. "Hiya. What are you doing here?"

"I might ask you the same question,"

Continued overleaf...

Continued from previous page

I said, hurrying down the stairs. "I got your message. I thought..."

I looked at Mark standing with his arm draped over her shoulder. If they'd had a row, they weren't showing any sign of it.

"You said something about the wedding. You were practically howling!"

"That's right." She carried on beaming. "It's all changed. You'll never guess what. Although as you're here, you

"Er... hi, Ian..." I said. "Lovely to see you. Must dash..."

I made a bolt for the door, but Ian reached out and grabbed my arm, spinning me round. I looked up – and up. Gone was the skinny nineteen-year-old with scruffy brown hair and angry-young-man eyes and in his place was a beautiful man, tall and broad-shouldered with gleaming chestnut hair and eyes that twinkled. Twinkled? Was he actually laughing?

His hair was damp, he smelled gorgeous and he was looking decidedly cross

probably already know."

"Know what? Who's in your bath?"

I looked over my shoulder. I could hear the bath water running away.

"Ian is not only going to be at the wedding, he's going to be Mark's best man. And you know what the old tradition is about chief bridesmaids and best men." Her smile couldn't get any bigger if it was made of elastic.

The bathroom door opened and I looked up to see Ian coming down the stairs. His hair was damp, he smelled gorgeous and he looked cross.

"My computer!" he said. "Victoria Bradshaw! Amelia Taylor!"

"Hi, Siddie," he said in a high squeaky voice. He was grinning.

Only Ian had ever shortened my name to Siddie. Hearing it again after all this time turned my legs to jelly.

"It's good to see you," he said in his normal, deep voice. "Really good."

Oh – not half as good as it was for me to see him!

"Is it?" I swallowed hard.

"Isn't it wonderful?" Jenny was crying again. "Ian's not just back for the wedding. He's *back* back!"

"Back back?"

"Back for good." He grinned.

It was time to crack open the wine. It seemed we'd be celebrating after all.

"This started with Cressida arriving with wine and cake – then suddenly I realised it wasn't who Cressida thought it was in the bathroom. The story just grew from there!"

Brain BOOSTERS

Missing Link

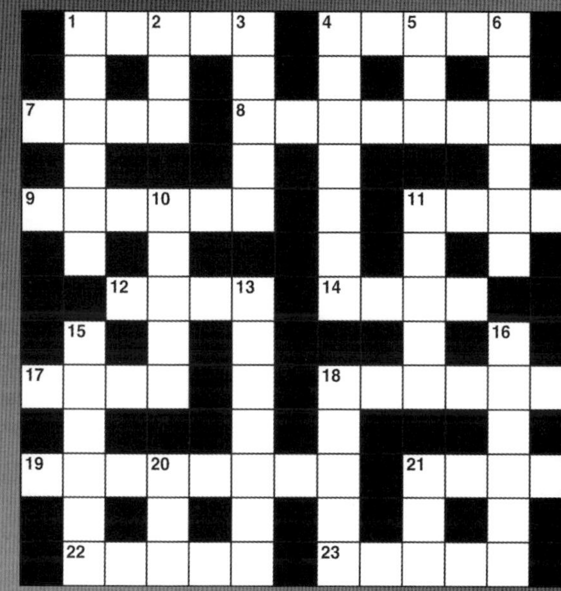

The answer to each clue is a word which has a link with each of the three words listed. This word may come at the end (eg **HEAD** linked with **BEACH, BIG, HAMMER**), at the beginning (eg **BLACK** linked with **BEAUTY, BOARD** and **JACK**) or a mixture of the two (eg **STONE** linked with **HAIL, LIME** and **WALL**).

ACROSS

1. Back, Gin, Shot (5)
4. Pocket, Stop, Tower (5)
7. Ear, Stick, Super (4)
8. Course, Ground, Weight (8)
9. Bleeding, Desire, Lonely (6)
11. Olive, Tomato, Wellington (4)
12. Hyacinth, Light, Spring (4)
14. Back, Step, Trap (4)
17. Hour, Job, Sugar (4)
18. Head, Jack, Yellow (6)
19. Column, Injury, Organiser (8)
21. Buzz, Cross, Perfect (4)
22. Meat, Pie, Soya (5)
23. Free, Hair, Life (5)

DOWN

1. Lining, Quick, Solid (6)
2. Breaker, Cube, Dry (3)
3. Factory, Flood, Sluice (5)
4. Around, Gift, Shrink (7)
5. Biscuit, Foil, Tack (3)
6. Cliff, Clothes, Coat (6)
10. Book, Copy, Estimate (5)
11. Cupboard, Handle, Stick (5)
13. Bank, Sheet, Spring (7)
15. British, Piece, Science (6)
16. Course, Honorary, Third (6)
18. Arm, Key, Loop (5)
20. Rising, Spot, Stroke (3)
21. Cause, High, Laid (3)

Solutions On Page 165

Perchance To Dream

Step into a lush Pre-Raphaelite world of young love denied, emotions running amok and secret plotting gone awry…

By Hayley Johnson-Mack

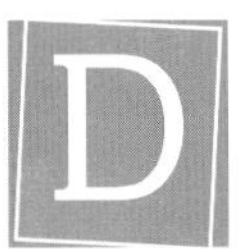

Drawing a last, lingering note from his violin, music master Rowan Isles lowered the bow and gave a sigh. "You are not listening."

His student turned her face from the window to smile sweetly at him, but Rowan wasn't fooled.

Miss Viola Whitcliffe always had something going on behind those huge, fawn-like eyes. At eighteen, in prim buttoned-up gowns, she had a bewitching innocent beauty about her. Imagine what she would be like in a few years' time…

"I was," she protested, pouting prettily. "But I could never play as beautifully as you do, Master Isles, so it sometimes seems a waste of time to practise."

Rowan hid a grin at her flattery.

"I disagree," he replied, "and more importantly, so would your father."

The tiny crinkle that appeared between her brows whenever her will was thwarted now made a bow.

"Then I suppose we had better continue." She sighed. "Even though the sun shines so brightly outside."

"Shall we pause a while?" Rowan suggested, no longer able to resist the entreaty in her eyes. "I'll go and give my progress report to your father."

Viola was already on her feet, good humour restored.

"And what will you say to him?"

Rowan strove to adopt a stern, magisterial manner.

"Could try harder."

"And I promise I shall do so." She laughed as she flitted to the window to peer hopefully outside. "After a little air."

Rowan knew precisely why his pupil was so desperate to embrace the sunshine, and no good could come of it, if her father was the single-minded man Rowan believed him to be. Professor Silas Whitcliffe heartily approved of the man currently paying court to Viola; he was simply the wrong one in her own opinion.

Viola's suitor, approved by her father, was the wrong man in her own opinion

He looked sadly at the discarded violins. If music be the food of love, Viola would embrace it with all her heart. As it was, he'd have to satisfy himself with teaching her the rudiments.

Continued overleaf…

If only Viola shared his passion for music

Continued from previous page

Rowan paused for a moment in the foyer of the professor's mansion, drawn as always to the painting hung above the fireplace. It was an interpretation of a Pre-Raphaelite piece entitled *Ophelia*, a depiction of Shakespeare's tragic heroine lying surrounded by flowers in a watery bed. Viola's face replaced that of the master's original model. A strange gift for a girl, perhaps, but meant as a tribute by her doting Papa, a man who was much more comfortable within the world of botany than that of parenting.

"To sleep, perchance to dream…"

A woman of a deeper, deadlier beauty than Viola's, with hair of burnished flame and eyes like a stalking cat's, drifted forward to stand beside Rowan. It was the professor's sister, Lilleth.

"Admiring the artwork, Master Isles? Or my niece?"

"In actual fact I was wondering how someone had succeeded in keeping her still for long enough to paint her."

Her laugh was like warm burgundy wine sliding down the throat.

"You know her well." She looked up at the painting. "Poor Ophelia. All that wasted innocence. Have you read Hamlet?" When Rowan shook his head, she said, "Then we must remedy that. Though I warn you, it's a desperate tale. The hero is a vengeful royal haunted by his father's ghost, his kingdom in turmoil and characters seeking to declare their prince mad."

"I'll come prepared."

She smiled; Rowan had the sudden unsettling feeling that she knew exactly what amoral thoughts were running through his mind, and moreover, was glad she had put them there.

"You'll not get away with this treachery, Silas! It was my creation – mine!"

He sucked in chilly air as he strode through the gardens in search of Professor Whitcliffe, needing extra in his lungs after his encounter with the intoxicating Lilleth. The death of Viola's mother having coincided with her own husband's fatal illness, Lilleth had relinquished her independence to take care of Silas's household.

Now a rich widow, she was able to indulge a love of art and literature, and the house had become a Mecca for aspiring artists and poets who flocked to her soirées and readings, hoping to secure her patronage.

He was jerked from his thoughts by the sound of raised voices coming from the first of a row of Whitcliffe's treasured Victorian glasshouses, where all his plant work and experiments took place.

"You'll not get away with this treachery, Silas! It was my creation – mine!"

"Get out, Alec, and take your ridiculous lies with you!"

"You've not heard the last of this!"

Rowan stepped aside just in time as a tall man he recognised as Alec Bailey, Whitcliffe's fellow botanist and on-off partner, erupted from the glasshouse and stormed off down the path. Silas, dark hair and beard flecked with soil as well as silver, followed to shout out to his gardener, "Don't let Bailey in again, Weekes! He's no longer welcome."

Alec's only response was a growl flung

over his shoulder. Silas shook a fist at him then, noticing the music teacher, straightened up with an effort at dignity.

"Ah, Isles. Were you looking for me?"

"Yes, sir," replied Rowan. "But I could return later if you are occupied."

As Whitcliffe seemed hardly to have heard him, his attention already re-focused on whatever disputed plant was nestling in the glasshouse, Rowan deemed it prudent to return to his lesson.

Another man was studying Viola's portrait when Rowan came back through the foyer. Aubrey Duval was the professor's bank manager, and also his choice of husband for his impressionable daughter. Duval acknowledged the music teacher with a stately nod, thick brows meeting in the centre of his forehead.

Rowan returned the gesture then continued on his way, wondering how such an intelligent man as Silas Whitcliffe could believe that a vibrant young woman like Viola could be content married to such a worthy bore as Mr Duval.

A silky-haired youth was declaiming poetry to a captive drawing-room audience, Lilleth included, when Rowan was finally ready to leave. He was about to pluck his coat from the stand when, for the second time that day, he heard his employer's voice raised in anger.

This time, it was aimed at Bailey's son Heath, a handsome young entrepreneur built on the same strapping lines as his father. He was imploring Silas to listen to him, to consider Viola's feelings.

"You insolent dog!" Silas stormed. "My daughter is my own to guide in this God-forsaken world we live in. And a bud must be nurtured before it can burst into flower. Too much light and it will bolt; too little, it will not bloom at all."

"Please, sir," Heath begged. "Let me see her."

"Heath?" Viola's baffled voice came from the stairs, where she stood clutching the banister. "What are you doing?"

"We are banished from here," Heath explained. "And I wish to take you away with me before you are bullied into marrying someone you do not love."

Viola looked nervously from father to lover. "This isn't what we planned."

"Exactly!" Silas crowed. "Now get out of my house and tell your father to bury his fantasies in the soil. See whether anything germinates!"

"Have a care," Heath warned. "Blind men have a habit of walking into pits."

Continued overleaf...

Continued from previous page

The door slammed as he departed.

On a sob, Viola fled back upstairs, leaving Silas to fume his way back to his precious glasshouse. Rowan saw Lilleth in the drawing-room doorway, her disciples and one frowning Aubrey Duval at her back.

"Now, that," she told her poet, "is how you do drama."

The party dispersed quickly after that. "See whether Mr Whitcliffe is to keep Mr Duval company at supper, would you, Margaret?" Lilleth asked a hovering maid. "If not, have his evening posset sent to the glasshouse." And to Rowan, "Will you come to my parlour? We have matters to discuss."

Lilleth motioned for Rowan to sit in one of two hearth chairs. Taking the other, she asked, "How has Viola seemed to you lately?"

"Just as always," Rowan replied. "Charming, sometimes not as diligent as I would like, but then, not everyone is as enslaved to music as I."

"Enslaved…" Lilleth sighed."Did you hear why Alec Bailey has been exiled? He accused Silas of stealing his latest hybrid and marketing it under the Whitcliffe name."

Rowan frowned.

"It is true?"

"Who knows? They think on such similar lines, it is not surprising if they dispute ownership of ideas. My brother is a good man, Master Rowan, but blind and completely archaic in his views where women are concerned. Viola watched both her mother and me lock horns with him to fight for our choice of future – and fail. She will go about securing her own quite differently."

"With Heath Bailey? But I thought her half-promised to Mr Duval."

"Yet can you see Viola wanting to marry such a man, especially when being wooed by a much more dashing model?"

"It is not for me to say," replied Rowan diplomatically. "I am merely her teacher."

His heart began to race as Lilleth moved purposefully in his direction.

"Well, tonight, shall I teach you a little something?" Her smile was slow and teasing as she reached behind him to pluck a book from the fireplace nook. "*Hamlet*, a tragedy, in the words of William Shakespeare…"

It was late when Rowan finally left, by the back stairs to save his blushes. Again, he needed air to chase away the spell Lilleth had woven on his senses. She had read to him of the infamous Prince Hamlet, but it was her presence rather than the plot that had held him enthralled.

He was peering through the darkness for the rear gate that would take him to the street when he saw a sturdy figure slipping out that way. Mistrusting its furtive manner, Rowan quickened his pace to follow, and promptly tripped over an obstruction sprawled across the path. Cursing, he stopped to see what he had stumbled on.

It was Silas Whitcliffe.

As night fell, the quiet that follows chaos descended on the house.

Silas, unconscious and breathing with difficulty, had been carried to his room and a doctor hastily summoned. Rowan remained to answer questions. How had Mr Whitcliffe been found? Face down on the garden path. How did he appear? Dead, at first glance. Did he respond at all when moved? Not a groan or a blink from garden to bedchamber. How would you explain the bump on his head? He fell heavily, perhaps. Was anyone with him when he fell? A pause, then, No, there was no-one with him.

The doctor was suspicious. Inwardly, so was Rowan. Whitcliffe's collapse was unnatural; some guiding hand had been the cause.

Lilleth and Viola were arm-in-arm on the sofa, Duval propping up the mantelpiece, when Rowan entered the drawing-room. Lilleth looked paler than Rowan had ever seen her. Her voice remained firm, however, as she said, "Thank you for your help, Master Isles."

Tears had left red tracks on Viola's cheeks. "Is Papa still unconscious?"

"More heavily asleep now," Rowan replied. "Though he has suffered some considerable trauma."

"Not surprising," remarked Duval, "after today's dramas. Has anyone spoken to the Baileys?"

"Why would they?" Viola demanded. "Papa has been working too hard. How could either of the Baileys be to blame for that?"

"By goading him to breaking point, perhaps? Or trying to turn his daughter's head with empty promises? We all heard young Bailey's threats."

"How dare you! You know nothing about Heath – or me!"

"Viola..." Lilleth said warningly.

Duval snorted. "Your father was right. You are gullible."

Viola sprang to her feet; Lilleth was there before her, holding her back.

"It has been a long day, and tempers fray when we are tired. Perhaps we should all seek our beds."

Duval immediately apologised and bowed himself out of the room. Viola waited until he had left before she headed upstairs, tell-tale crinkle set firmly between her brows.

"How dare you! You know nothing about Heath – or me!" Viola cried out

Rowan was left alone with Lilleth. There was worry in her face, and something else that made him pause.

"You know, do you not?" she asked.

"That Silas was drugged with a high dose of opium poppy?" Rowan nodded. "How did it happen?"

"The doctor thinks it had been added to something he drank; his posset, most likely."

"Who would know how to use that plant to render Silas unconscious?" Rowan wondered.

Continued overleaf...

Continued from previous page

"This is a botanist's house," said Lilleth dryly. "Ask rather, who would not. That includes the Baileys."

"Passionate tempers like theirs don't plan ahead; they strike first and think later. And what would be the point of drugging him, anyway, unless they anticipated his having an adverse reaction that could kill him?"

"Kill him?" Lilleth started. "No! Believe me, despite their fallouts, Silas and Alec are kindred spirits. They cannot live without each other."

"I saw a man at the gate earlier," Rowan now revealed. "I thought it was Heath, but it could just as easily have been Alec. If he truly believed Silas had stolen his idea, he had a strong reason for revenge. To add fuel to the fire, his son was thrown out of the house earlier."

"That was more because Silas has finally realised that Viola is rather too fond of Heath."

Rowan frowned.

"And how would the man intended for her react to that? After tonight's display, I'd say Duval is capable of securing what he believed was his. But what would he achieve by attacking Silas? And would he know what to use? No; regrettably, I think we must look elsewhere for our druggist."

A flicker of her usual fascination returned to Lilleth's face.

"So deductive, Master Isles. You are wasted as a violinist."

"Then it is your fault," Rowan returned. "My head is full of Danish treason."

"Well, I for one think we have had enough scheming."

Lilleth rose to open the door. Over her shoulder, the painted Viola slumbered on in her watery bed, surrounded by multi-coloured flowerheads – and, yes, a bright red poppy.

"To sleep," Rowan muttered soberly. "Perchance, to dream..."

He did not return to the house until the following afternoon, having overslept after lying awake all night. Relieved to hear that Silas was recovering, he remained grave as he went to find Viola. Those restless hours had helped him understand just why Silas had been drugged.

Viola looked wan and heavy-eyed but made an effort to smile for Rowan.

"Have you come to practise scales?"

Rowan shook his head, then surprised Viola by kneeling to gently take her hand. "You must not worry any more. Your father will recover."

Tears started to well in Viola's eyes. But before she could speak, the door opened to admit Lilleth.

"Master Isles, may I speak with you?"

Leading Rowan to her parlour, Lilleth offered him the same chair as before.

"Still wondering about Silas?" she asked as she seated herself opposite. "Let me put your mind at rest. I gave him the poppy dose. I meant only to make him take some rest before he did some damage, to himself or someone else. I never dreamed that it would affect him so profoundly."

Rowan said nothing for a moment. Then, "It won't work. But I admire you for

Lilleth smiled. "So deductive, Master Isles. You are wasted as a violinist"

trying to protect someone you love."

She eyed him through veiled lashes.

"What can you mean?"

His smile was grim.

"That I've had time to think things through, and understand what happened. Bailey – Heath Bailey – lurking in the garden, Silas drugged for no obvious reason, and a painting where tragic Ophelia lies dying of unrequited love. Viola could metaphorically suffer the same fate if her father persists in marrying her to Duval, for whom she clearly bears little affection, particularly after last night. We know she has a strong will, yet up to now, she's seemed submissive.

"You said yourself that no good comes of directly opposing Silas. So what if she and Heath secretly resolved to elope? That explains why she was so complacent; she was already sure of her future. But then Silas argued with the Baileys, Heath panicked and brought their love affair into the open. Silas was now acutely aware of Viola's true feelings. That is what she meant when she said, 'This isn't planned'.

"With her future with Heath now in jeopardy, Viola becomes desperate to go to him. So she resorts to a little poppy syrup to ensure her suspicious Papa sleeps through her escape. Only she is nervous, so she gives him too strong a dose. Silas turns out to be excessively sensitive to the drug and falls into a coma. No wonder she was beside herself. First, she feared she'd killed her father, then Duval accused Heath of the crime! She almost gave herself away last night before you stepped in to prevent her.

"Now you bring me here and 'confess' yourself, so that Viola is protected from whatever action you think I may take."

Lilleth's smile was unreadable.

"What an imagination. If Viola had indeed drugged her father, I should be wondering how to buy your silence."

"No need," Rowan murmured. "Silas is recovering, Viola penitent, so what good would come of involving the law?"

"You still refuse to believe it was me?"

When Rowan merely smiled, Lilleth ran her tongue across her lower lip. "I am flattered, music master. If only there was a way to show you how much."

Rowan glanced down at the hand she'd placed on his knee.

"Oh, you are dangerous, you Whitcliffe women," he whispered. Then he rose and, lifting her hand, pressed a kiss upon it. "Alas, I am no match for your wiles."

Lilleth sat staring at the door long after Master Isles had closed it behind him, a wistful smile on her lips. At last, she stood, shook out her skirts and crossed to the hearth. From her pocket she retrieved a little glass phial, then, with a sigh, tipped the remainder of its contents onto the flames...

THE AUTHOR SAYS...

"This story came about through exploring the effects of a parent with fixed ideas for their child's future, and the intriguing tale behind the creation of a famous Pre-Raphaelite painting..."

So When We Meet

Why was I putting myself through this agony? I'd pushed it out of my mind for all these years – should I have let it lie?

By Sandra Woolfenden

ut it's only six o'clock," my husband Mark complains. "No need to get up yet, surely."

"I've been awake for ages," I tell him. "I thought I might as well do the ironing."

He grunts and turns over. My stomach feels as though it has frogs leaping around in it. I hadn't expected to be so nervous. I've been awake most of the night watching the clock go round.

I wish I'd never started the process – and then again, I'm excited. Anxious, too, wondering if I'm doing the right thing. After all these years.

I make myself a mug of tea and sit with it, wrapping my hands around the warmth. The house feels very quiet, and now I'm up, I'm actually too tired to face the ironing.

I take my tea with me back to bed. Mark is fast asleep. I sip my tea and half way through find I don't want it. I really ought to get some sleep. I've a two-hour drive ahead of me and I don't want to be tired. Fighting the restlessness, I cuddle up to Mark's back for comfort. I'm turned away from the bedside clock now and vow I won't look at it any more.

I drift off into a half sleep, and then I hear the shower running. I turn over and allow myself to look at the clock. It's a quarter to eight. Helen is up.

I slip quietly out of bed and into my dressing gown. I wonder how Helen feels about the coming meeting. I'm glad, now, that she shot down my arguments for going alone.

"Even if it doesn't work out," she says sympathetically, "you'll have tried"

"You might need me," she told me with all the wisdom of her fifteen years.

I gave in easily because I realised I didn't want to travel alone. Helen has such a positive attitude.

"Even if it doesn't work out," she said sympathetically, "at least you'll have tried and you'll have satisfied your curiosity."

"Yes," I agreed. "I haven't told her that you'll be coming with me."

"No need," Helen insisted, grinning. "She'll get two for the price of one."

PICTURES: ISTOCKPHOTO, THINKSTOCK ILLUSTRATION: JIM DEWAR

My daughter has such a positive attitude

Helen comes out of the bathroom, her dark hair wrapped in a towel. She looks so pretty, my daughter, so relaxed. I take my turn in the bathroom to have a shower, wondering what to wear, although I laid out my clothes last night. I've plenty of time so I could change my mind.

Yes, I'm doubtful about everything – even what to wear, which is ridiculous. But I want it to be right; smart but not over the top. My black trouser suit and white top will be fine, I tell myself.

"You look nice," Helen comments kindly when I emerge in the kitchen. She's dressed in a pair of jeans and a bright red T-shirt. I wish I had her composure.

"I'm just making some toast," she informs me jauntily. "Interested?"

"I'm not really hungry," I apologise, "and we're having lunch out, aren't we?"

"I can't wait that long!" she declares. "Did you remember to get any lime marmalade?"

Continued overleaf...

Continued from previous page

"Yes." I smile.

"You're such a good mother," she tells me and plants an unexpected kiss on my cheek.

She knows somehow that today I need reassurance and she's prepared to use rare flattery to give it to me. I'm grateful she thinks I'm a good mother.

I acknowledge to myself how lucky I am to have her for a daughter.

We're meeting at one o'clock so if I leave by eleven, we can have a leisurely drive there. The idea is to meet half-way on neutral ground. I'll park near the railway station to meet the train, and then we can walk the short distance to the restaurant I've chosen for lunch. I ring and check they have the reservation and inform them it is now for three.

Mark gets up and says, "I'll come with you if you like, drive you there."

"No." I laugh. "I can't change the table booking again. It's no big deal."

He's not fooled. He knows it is a very big deal, something I thought I'd never do.

So why *am* I doing it? Why the change of heart?

It all began with Helen's friend, Jade. Jade is adopted. The thing is that, at fifteen, she has no hang-ups about it, none at all. She doesn't mind who knows.

"I expect my mother had a very good reason for parting with me," she said, helping herself to another biscuit. "I don't feel resentful towards her."

I admired her maturity. "You wouldn't want to see her, though?"

Jade thought about it. "I think I would like to see her. I'd like to know if I look like her, if she likes sport like I do, things like that. If she tried to trace me and wanted to meet up, I'd agree. Or one day I'll maybe try and get in touch with her."

"It might be a complete disaster," I pointed out.

She shrugged. "Then we both just say, 'Nice to have met you, goodbye.'"

I liked her interpretation of how easy it would be but also felt she had over-simplified it. Surely, for all she said, there was a deeply buried resentment. Surely there must be times when she questioned why her mother parted with her. Could she truly not be judgmental?

Later, Helen had questions of her own. "You were very interested in the fact that Jade is adopted, Mum. Why was that?"

My resolve to keep my secret broke and I told her the truth. She was stunned.

"Does Dad know?"

"Of course. I told him long before we got married."

"I'm glad I know now. What are you going to do about it?"

"Nothing," I said, but I didn't sound or feel absolutely definite.

"There's bound to be websites that can put people in touch," she said. "I'll look into it for you, if you like."

We discussed it with Mark and he raised no objection if it was what I wanted to do.

So here I am still watching the clock, still wondering obsessively whether I'm doing the right thing.

It's ten minutes to eleven. And suddenly it's time to go. As I turn the key

"You look scared to death." She giggles. Good job you have me with you..."

in the ignition, doubts flood my brain. I've pushed it to the back of my mind for so long; why hadn't I left it there? I could have made up some excuse when Helen questioned me.

Yet that wouldn't have been fair. It wouldn't have been fair to any of us. And as Jade so casually put it, we can simply say, "Nice to have met you, goodbye".

There she was, waving her umbrella

"You look scared to death." Helen giggles as I pull up at the traffic lights. "Good job you have me with you."

"I'm fine." I deny it.

"I wonder if she's all nervous too," Helen says. "I bet she is."

Funny, I hadn't even thought of that. It calms me a little. On my own, I might well have had second thoughts and rung through an excuse not to meet, turned around and gone home to the safety of Helen and Mark.

We reach the station twenty minutes early. It's been an unbelievably long day already and it is not even lunchtime. I hope the train isn't late. I want to get this over with.

Supposing the train is crowded and we don't find her? Or maybe she has changed her mind and won't turn up. She said she would carry a plaid umbrella and would wave it about. The train pulls in. Helen squeezes my hand; I smile at her.

"Look!" Helen shrieks, "There she is waving a brolly like someone demented!"

We run towards the umbrella and I see her clearly. Even without the umbrella, I would have recognised her. There is a strong family resemblance between the three of us. It's uncanny.

For a few seconds we look at each other and then my usually so-cool daughter, overcome with emotion, starts to cry. Then we're all crying and hugging. And I know it's going to be all right despite the tears – or maybe even because of them.

"This is Helen," I say to the woman who gave birth to me. "Your granddaughter."

THE AUTHOR SAYS...

"At one time there was little encouragement or help to keep an illegitimate baby. How heartbreaking it must have been for the mother to part with her child."

Morning Glory

There's nothing wrong with healthy competition – unless it's overshadowing the tender shoots of a new friendship

By Wendy Kremer

ood morning, Bert."

"Morning, Ida." He touched his cloth cap. "Entering anything in the show this year, then, are you?"

She straightened her shoulders, moving her shopping basket to a more comfortable position. "I expect so."

"And you're not worried? If the same thing happens as last year, then it won't be worth your efforts."

She answered primly. "Last year was last year. If I hadn't had such bad luck with blight, you wouldn't have ended up in the centre of all those photos, so stop smirking all over your face."

Bert's eyes were wide and innocent.

"Don't know what you mean, Ida."

"Then I won't waste time explaining. I'll just warn you not to count your chickens before they're hatched."

"Chickens? I'm not entering chickens, Ida – just marrows, potatoes, tomatoes and roses."

With heightened colour, Ida studied her neighbour for a second, then went on her way without another word.

Bert took off his cap, scratched his head and chuckled as he watched the slender figure disappear round the corner.

A day or two later, Bert rubbed his forehead with a much-used red spotted hankie and looked up at a sunny cloudless sky. The sun was good for some things in the garden, but bad for others. He regarded some of the rose petals with a knowing eye. They were looking good, some of the best he'd ever had, but there was no point in entering them; Ida's were in a class of their own.

His roses were looking good, but there was no point entering them in the show

The tomatoes were perfect, though. They had a bright red colour and they tasted wonderful. He was still feeding the marrows with his special formula, and his hopes were growing at the same rate as the marrows. He wasn't sure about the potatoes yet, and didn't intend to pull them until it was just the right time. The

Continued overleaf...

ILLUSTRATIONS: THINKSTOCK, KIRK HOUSTON

Preparations for the show were under way

Continued from previous page

tops looked green and healthy, but no one could tell what was going on underneath, in the dark.

On the way home from his allotment he slowed his pace as he passed Ida's garden. Over the fence, he couldn't see in detail any of the things he wanted to see, but he did admire the perfectly ordered flowerbeds and tidy lawn.

A delicious aroma of meat pie drifted towards him. Give Ida her due; she wasn't just a magician in the garden, she'd always been a good cook, too.

Heading towards his empty, silent house, he wondered if there was anything in the fridge worth eating. If not, he'd have to go down the pub for a meal again.

Bert thought about the rivalry between him and Ida. It was a leftover from the days when her husband Ron was alive. He and Ron had always been rivals; that went back to the days when they were young and after the same girls. Ida had been one of those girls, and Ron had won her over. Something in Bert had never accepted that. His friendship with Ron ended abruptly and a few years later they restarted their rivalry – at the local show.

He'd married Stella soon after. She'd been a good wife and they'd had a happy marriage. Now Ron and Stella were both gone, but the rivalry at the show went on.

He shook his head. He had to admit that after all this time, it was silly. Ida and he were acting like a couple of stupid kids.

The days sped by, and Ida and Bert spent more time than ever in their respective gardens. Bert saw her most mornings on his way to the allotment.

"Morning, Ida. Everything okay?"

She clutched at the base of her spine as she straightened up.

"Oh, it's you, Bert. Yes, fine. And you?"

"Good! Ready for the show on Saturday?"

"As ready as I'll ever be."

Bert touched his cap. "I'll be on my way then. Got to start giving water before it gets too warm."

Ida nodded understandingly. "Yes, you have to be spot on. If you miss the right moment, it all goes haywire."

"Yes, you're right there."

Bert carried his entries in their various containers into the tent and fished in his pockets for the labels he'd written with such care. He handed the personal details of his entries to the man in charge, who was another neighbour. He then placed the numbers he'd been given in exchange, next to his produce.

Finally satisfied with organising his own display, he took time to look at some of the other entries. Passing a table with some other tomatoes and a bunch of terrific peach-coloured roses, he recognised Ida's handwriting.

For a moment, he was overcome by a feeling of triumph; even he could tell his tomatoes were better.

The feeling died quickly because he'd been thinking about Ida a lot recently. He'd recalled the days when he'd been in love with her. She was still a good-looking woman today. But she'd had a hard life had Ida. Ron had died years ago and

She was still a good-looking woman, although he knew she'd had a hard life

she'd had to struggle ever since to make ends meet.

He looked around. The neighbour in charge was talking to someone in the tent entrance. There was no one else in sight. He picked up Ida's tomatoes and crossed the tent swiftly. He picked up his own and replaced them with Ida's, leaving his label in place, and took his tomatoes back to Ida's display next to her own neat label.

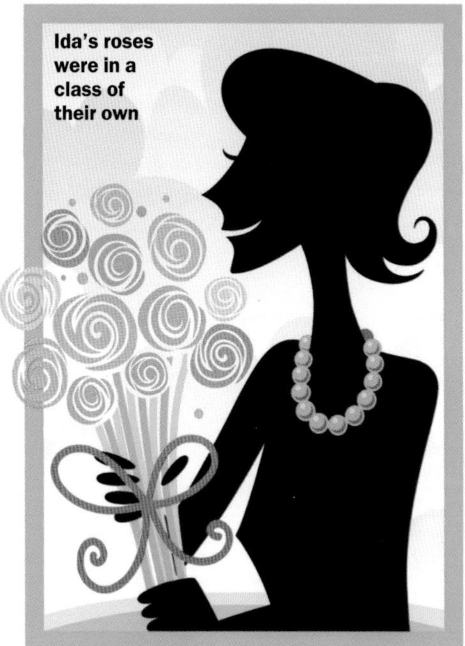
Ida's roses were in a class of their own

Ida beamed as the photographer's flashlight blazed and the local reporter took down the details that would appear in next week's column. Bert watched from a distance. He'd won first prize for his marrow and a second for his potatoes. He was satisfied, and he also had a warm feeling inside. She deserved it.

Making his way to the entrance, getting some encouraging claps on his shoulder as he went, he caught Ida's eye and gave her a thumbs-up.

He was half way across the village green when she called after him.

"Bert, wait. Are you going home?"

Surprised, Bert looked up and nodded.

She hurried to join him. She had her products in a basket and her prize roses filled her arms.

"I was just wondering. What do you think about us putting these roses on Ron and Stella's graves, and then you and I making some sandwiches with these tomatoes?" She lifted the bag. "*Your* tomatoes!"

Bert saw the laughter in her blue eyes. He began to chuckle and Ida joined in.

"Aren't we a couple of stupid old cronies?" she asked.

He nodded and tucked her arm through his as they walked towards the entrance of the nearby churchyard.

Ron and Stella were buried in the same row. Ida and Bert arranged the roses in the respective vases and stood for a while next to both of the graves, remembering.

Bert was the first to turn away, leaving Ida by her husband's grave. A few minutes later, she joined him on his bench alongside the church. The sun was going down now and it threw a golden sheen across the churchyard.

Bert broke the silence. "It's hard sometimes, isn't it?"

"Yes, I often think how unfair life is. Ron was a good man and he didn't deserve to die so young."

"You didn't deserve to be left alone."

"I learned to accept it, and I learned to

Continued overleaf...

Continued from previous page

cope. Do you miss Stella very much? I liked her; she was a nice woman. She never let the rivalry in our gardens stop her chatting and asking how I was."

"Yes, I do. During the day it's not so bad, there are always things to do, but in the evenings it's much too quiet."

She nodded. "I know what you mean. Sometimes I talk to Ron's picture. It helps when I have a problem. It gives me a feeling he's still part of my life."

"It was a good show today, wasn't it? Your roses swept the board. You have a hand for roses."

"I wish I could say the same for my tomatoes. Whatever made you swap mine for yours? I could tell straight away that they were yours. No one else manages to get that colour, or that gloss."

Bert coughed, a little embarrassed.

"I started to think how stupid we've been through the years. Instead of remaining friends, we were always rivals."

Her eyes twinkled. "My daughter said the same thing."

"Maureen said that? Then she's a lot cleverer than we were."

For a moment they listened to the birds singing and the soft sound of someone playing the organ in the church.

Ida brushed her skirt and picked up the basket with the rest of her show entries. "What about those tomatoes? Would you like a sandwich?"

Clearing his throat, Bert replied, "I'd prefer them sliced with just some salt and vinegar on a plate, if you don't mind. They're too good to stick between two pieces of bread. You don't taste them properly if they're in a sandwich."

She smiled. "You're right! Come on then. There's a good quiz show on tonight. Fancy watching it with me?"

He picked up his sack of items and a smile split his wrinkled face in two. "Can't think of anything I'd enjoy more."

They started off down the road.

"Ida, how about the Chelsea Flower Show? Have you ever been there?"

"Once. It was very interesting."

"I started to think how stupid we've been through the years, always rivals"

"How about going together this year? We can get new ideas, pick up some tips."

Ida felt there was a spring in her step again. "Yes, I think I'd like that.."

He nodded. "There's a flower show in Lower Noxhead next Saturday. Shall we take a look? Who knows, if we combine our knowledge and enter things there next year, we could sweep the board."

Their chatter drifted through the air. It travelled back through the lynch gate and across the silent gravestones.

There was peace and approval in the air as the last rays of golden sunshine touched the petals of the prize roses in the two vases, standing just a short distance apart.

THE AUTHOR SAYS...

"Life is sometimes rough on us; we feel cheated and at odds with destiny. Luckily, fate often redresses the balance for us in unexpected ways at unexpected times."

Fancy That!

Orange facts that make you go "**Wow!**"

If you drive an orange car it means you're fun loving and trendy!

Alexander the Great washed his hair in saffron to keep it orange– saffron was then more expensive than gold

◆ **True orange generally elicits a "love it or hate it" response in most people.**

◆ During the Elizabethan era only nobility were allowed to wear the colour orange.

◆ **It takes 50 glasses of water to grow enough oranges to make one glass of orange juice.**

◆ American Indians associate the colour orange with kinship.

◆ **The fruit came before the colour – the Arabic for the fruit, naranj, arrived in England as "norange" and eventually lost the initial "n".**

◆ The colour of an orange depends on where it's grown: in temperate climes its green skin turns orange when the weather cools, but in hotter countries it stays green.

◆ **The colour orange stimulates appetite and sociability.**

◆ There is a place called Orange County in the American state of California.

◆ **Aroma Pod, a scented lifestyle tool, uses the colour orange with the scent that provides awakening.**

◆ In China and Japan, orange is used to symbolise happiness and love.

◆ **Black flight boxes on aircraft are actually orange so they can be found more easily; they were called "black boxes" because early prototypes were black.**

Brazil grows a third of all oranges in the world, with 85% being used for juice

◆ In Spanish, anaranjear means literally to "orangicate" – to pelt something with oranges.

The first New World orange trees were planted in Florida in 1513 by Spanish explorer Juan Ponce de Leon

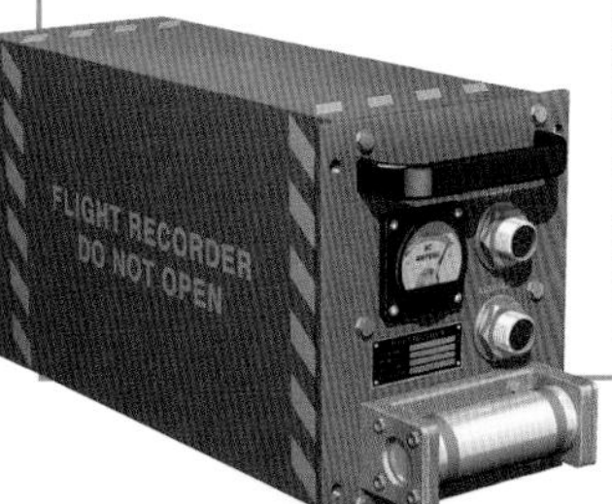

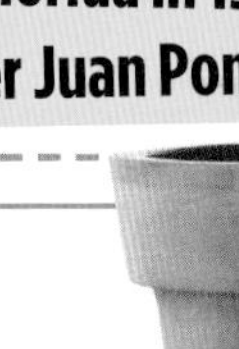

WORDS: BABS BEATON PICTURES: THINKSTOCK, ISTOCKPHOTO, ALAMY

In The Bluebell Wood

Love and hope can transcend so many things – and the gnarled old tree was the last link to my precious friend

By Sue Johnson

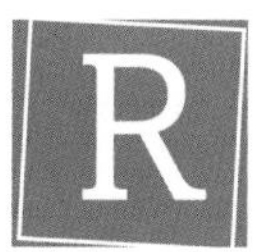

"Really, Doris," I imagine my mother saying. "Fancy behaving like that at your age."

"I don't care what you think," I whisper back into the darkness. "I've chained myself to Josie's wishing tree in the wood so they can't chop it down to build their bypass. It's all I have to remember her by."

Josie's family played in a stinking yard; her mum carted washing in an old pram

Mind you, I wish I'd brought a thicker blanket. It's a bleak December night. The fallen leaves are crisp as dry cornflakes and the ground's hard as iron.

I've never protested about anything before. I'm not that sort of person – Mother always discouraged me from drawing attention to myself.

In any case, some changes are for the best. I was glad when they renovated Mitchell's Buildings a few years ago. "Luxury Apartments" they are now, with block-paved drives, and owners with posh cars and plum-in the-mouth jobs.

It was once where Josie and her family lived. She and her brothers and sisters played in a stinking yard and their mother carted loads of washing in an old pram. Josie's mother never wore stockings, and her legs under the ragged hem of her skirt were knobbly as Brussels sprout stems.

Mother didn't encourage my friendship with Josie.

PICTURES: THINKSTOCK ILLUSTRATION: JIM DEWAR

The woods were Josie's favourite place

Continued from previous page

"You're not to go home with her," she said. "That place is full of germs."

Mitchell's Buildings was an old woollen mill. It smelled of rancid cooking fat and boiled cabbage. Josie, her mother, her brothers and sisters were crammed into two rooms. There was one outside toilet to six families; in summer the whole place hummed with bluebottles.

Josie had no father, but the number of her brothers and sisters grew steadily. Josie always had an answer for anyone who commented about this.

"Me dad comes and goes at strange times," she said confidently. "Sometimes he only has a few hours with Mum, and then he has to fly back to America to help round up the buffalo."

It wasn't always rounding up buffalo. Sometimes it was counting the gold bars before the Bank of England opened, or grooming horses for the Shah of Persia.

Miss Phipps, our teacher, said Josie was the best storyteller in the class.

"Of course," I heard her say to the headmistress, "not that it'll do Josephine any good. She'll go the same way as her mother before too long. I doubt if she'll even finish her schooling."

My mother couldn't bear to think that Josie's schoolwork was better than mine. She was furious when I took home a school report that said I was bottom of the class. She had high hopes of me getting an office job and not working in a factory when I left school.

"You can't be trying hard enough, Doris. I knew no good would come of you being friends with that Josephine Miller."

"But Josie came top," I said.

"How could she have done?" hissed my mother as she threw my report on the fire. "I've always given you every encouragement."

I remember taking home a picture I'd drawn of Blanding's Wood when the bluebells were out. Even Miss Phipps was impressed and had put it on the wall.

Josie thought it was beautiful.

"You could be an artist," she'd said, looking at the picture through half-closed eyes. "I can almost smell that lovely scent."

"It's not the sort of thing that'll get you a decent job or husband," said Mother, "and don't go letting that Josephine fill your head with nonsense. You can be gullible at times, Doris."

There were several questions Josie could never answer. Why, with all the fantastic jobs he had, did her dad never make enough money for Mrs Miller and the children to have nice food and warm clothes? Why did Mrs Miller have to take in washing, struggling with buckets of icy water from the single tap in the yard? Why did Josie wear the same cut-down cotton dress to school summer and winter, with no knickers or vest underneath? Why did she sometimes have no lunch?

Mother's mouth folded shut like crimped pastry when I asked if I could take some food to share with Josie at school dinner-time.

"You? An artist? Don't go letting that Josephine fill your head with nonsense"

"That girl will come to a bad end – you keep away from her," she said. "People like her aren't our responsibility."

I took no notice and shared my sandwiches with Josie – not just because I felt sorry for her, but because I loved her. If I could've chosen a sister she would have been just like Josie.

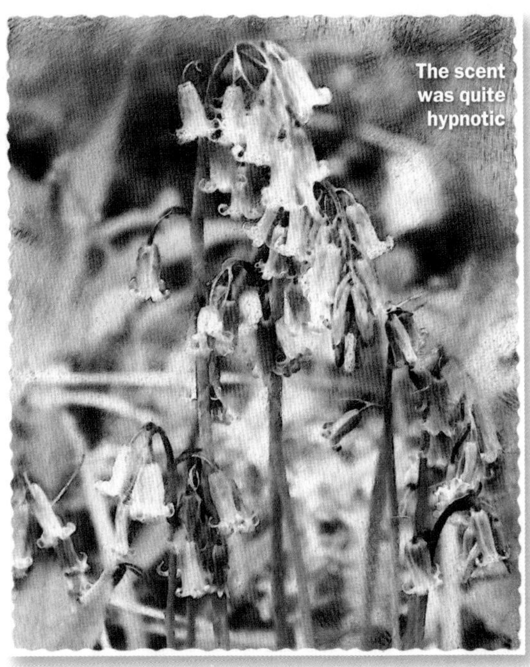
The scent was quite hypnotic

Sometimes in the winter, Josie's face was as pale as the milk she couldn't afford to drink. She shivered in her peach cotton dress and I wished I could give her one of my old woollen ones. At dinner-time she sat on the big heating pipes that snaked round the classroom, huddled like a frozen sparrow.

There were many times when she'd come to school looking flushed with temperature and with a hacking cough that sliced the chilly air. No matter how ill she looked, she never missed school.

"It's the best part of the day," she said, her face glowing, "apart from walking in the woods on the way home."

I remembered this now as I looked up at the moon and stars, my breath hanging in smoky clouds on the still air. My chest felt tight, but there was no way I was giving up.

The bulldozers were on their way – white lights flashed through the trees and the other protesters were chanting, "Save Blandings Wood."

Since that dreadful day just after her tenth birthday, I've come to Blanding's Wood every week to remember Josie and her stories.

The whole class was shocked when Josie didn't turn up for school. You see, it had never happened before. I knew she must be very ill indeed to miss her walk through the woods, especially now that the bluebells were in flower.

"Don't look so worried, Doris, she'll be better in a few days," said Miss Phipps.

I knew she was lying. I'd heard her whispering to another teacher about a diphtheria epidemic at Mitchell's Buildings and that the authorities should do something before it was too late.

On the way home from school, I went to the woods to pick bluebells for Josie. At the edges of the path, cow parsley grew higher than my head, reminding me of a white lace edging, and

Continued overleaf...

Continued from previous page

the smell of bluebells in the dappled shade of the wood was hypnotic.

Josie was sitting by the gnarled oak that she called her wishing tree.

"Miss Phipps said you were ill," I said.

Josie shrugged. "I'm better now."

I listened for the church clock to make sure I wasn't late for tea.

"You've got ages yet," said Josie.

We lay among the bluebells, breathing in their heady scent, and that's where I last saw her, her face looking peaceful in the place she loved.

I fell asleep amongst the bluebells and when I woke up, Josie had gone. I was late home; Mother gave me a good hiding and sent me to bed without any tea when I said I'd been talking to Josie in Blanding's Wood.

"That child died of diphtheria this morning. Don't you dare lie to me, Doris. How could you have seen her?"

It didn't matter how many special doctors Mother took me to, I know I saw Josie in Blanding's Wood that day. I've never stopped believing it, no matter what they did to me.

I can hear Josie's voice in my head clearly now, even though the trees in front of me look strange and shimmery and my chest hurts so much that I feel dizzy every time I take a breath.

"They'll not take this wood away from us, Doris." Josie's warm breath tickles my ear.

A few people have clustered round me asking anxious questions, their breath white on the still air and their boots

That was where I last saw her

crunching the frosted leaves. I try to tell them they should be blocking the bulldozers, not worrying about an old woman like me, but the words won't come.

"Call an ambulance," someone shouts. "This lady's not well."

A few minutes later the mournful wail of an ambulance siren cuts across the noise of the bulldozers. Flickering blue lights replace glaring white.

The world has a dreamlike quality – the trees are edged with silver, and I feel as if I'm seeing everything through the wrong end of a telescope.

Josie's standing in front of me now, her face radiant as she takes my hands in hers, blue eyes sparkling with magic.

"Come on, Doris. I've come to take you home. There's tea in the pot and fresh gingerbread in the oven – and me dad's home from counting all the kangaroos in Australia."

THE AUTHOR SAYS...

"I've always loved bluebells! The colour and smell are great inspiration for writing. They take me back to childhood and the woods I explored with my brother and other friends."

Brain BOOSTERS

Fun Word Wheel

You have ten minutes to find as many words as possible using the letters in the wheel. Each word must be three letters or more and contain the central letter. Use each letter once and no plurals, foreign words or proper nouns are allowed. There is at least one nine-letter word.

Average: 25 words
Good: 32 words
Excellent: 40 words

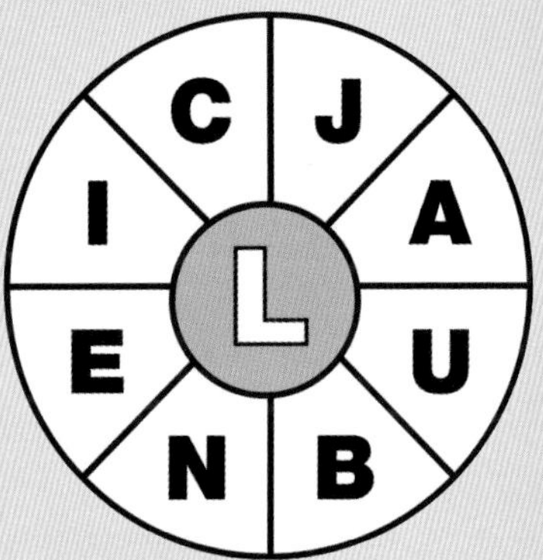

Two Sudoku

Fill in each of the blank squares with the numbers 1 to 9, so that each row, each column and each 3x3 cell contains all the numbers from 1 to 9.

Sudoku 1

		4						
	5		7	2	3			
6	7		8			9		
7	4						9	
				3			8	
	1	5	9			3	7	
		2	1					7
			2		8	4	1	
					4	8		

Sudoku 2

		7	8	5			9	
						1		7
		5		7	3		8	
	4				5		1	
	5					8		
	3				1		6	
		9		4	8		7	
						6		5
		4	5	6			2	

Solutions On Page 165

Apollo & Me

Life in the little thatched cottage was from a bygone age – all watched over by Grandma Betsy's enigmatic black cat

By Elsie Lloyd

There it stands, the *For Sale* sign displayed by the gate. The cottage is looking a little bit shabby now, and the thatch is darker than I remember it as it was as my childhood home. It appears so much smaller too, but I guess that's because I'm more in proportion now; a bit small for my age in those days, I shot up during my later teens.

Walking and half skipping all the way home held no fears for an eight-year-old, finishing the day at school in the village. On summer days, long light evenings, Emily would cut through the slowly ripening wheat fields and past the small stream. The two huge chestnut trees almost hid the little cottage that was her home for the time being.

Emily would head straight for the kitchen, where there was always the nicest of aromas. Grandma Betsy was busy making another batch of biscuits and a Victoria sponge was cooling on a rack, just waiting for Emily to fill it with homemade strawberry jam, and to dust the top with icing sugar.

The biscuits were Grandma's speciality. She made so many varieties – ginger, shortbread, Garibaldi and chocolate (when she could get a tin of cocoa) – the list was endless.

On market day in the village, a small table was laid out with boxes of her wares, and she would sell them at "five for a shilling". Everything would be sold out within a couple of hours, so then they would go on to buy all the ingredients for another week of baking.

An old pram would be brought into service, transporting everything to and from the village. Then at last they'd visit the old sweet shop, so that Emily could buy her favourite: large, striped, glistening humbugs.

The walk back to the cottage was spent almost in silence, as the humbugs, being slowly sucked, didn't allow Emily to say much; she would have to remove it to chat to Betsy, and then pop it back for some concentrated savouring. At home, one humbug could last for a couple of days, carefully wrapped in a handkerchief until ready for another blissful assault.

Grandma Betsy was very busy making another batch of biscuits – her speciality

Grandma Betsy had a cat, a large fluffy black cat, with huge green eyes and the most ornamental white whiskers which stood out in profusion from his cheeks, like porcupine quills – and almost as sharp.

He never needed to be fed by Grandma,

PICTURES: ISTOCKPHOTO ILLUSTRATIONS: KIRK HOUSTON

Grandma's cat was ever present

finding ample fare in the surrounding copse, fields and the garden; it was no wonder he was so big. His name was Apollo, a true God of all he surveyed.

He didn't go in for being cuddled – would tolerate being stroked, but not for long – then could sit for ages just watching his humans in silent contemplation. To Emily, he was also a very good listener.

Emily's homework would get done early in the evening, and while she was swift in her History, Geography and English, the Maths was always a battle. Apollo would sit on the windowsill, companionably listening as she worked out her sums, asking him all the questions but knowing she'd get no answer.

Grandma Betsy was no help with Maths, her knowledge being confined to "a spoonful of this", or "the weight of a couple of eggs be the same for the amount of butter" – things that were useful for the mouthwatering fare she made.

Sometimes the village kids would come over to play, and to some the silent cat and the ever-baking Betsy were grist for their imagination. Emily had to fend off their questions as to whether Betsy was a witch.

"Well, she's always mixing potions to cook in her kitchen, and she does have a great big black cat, doesn't she?"

By the back door stood an old yard broom, made of twigs tied to a long dry branch. Emily and Betsy found it perfect for sweeping up the fallen leaves from the two chestnut trees. This only stirred their young imaginations and, as most people called Grandma's tasty biscuits "love potions" meaning they always had a lovely feeling of pleasure after eating them, thoughts of witches persisted.

As she grew up, Emily helped in the baking process more and more. She had

Continued overleaf...

Continued from previous page

many recipes in her head, and Betsy was a good teacher. Neither felt the years slipping by; one growing up, the other growing old.

One morning during Emily's English lesson, not long before the school holidays, it was a bright day and the classroom windows were wide open, when they had an unexpected visitor.

Apollo suddenly appeared at the window, his huge bulk filling the sill. He looked around and, seeing Emily, jumped down and ran up and onto her desk. He started to purr loudly and pushing her in the face, rubbed himself against her. The class were delighted with these antics, but not so the teacher, who came over to take the cat away, and put him out, but Apollo would have none of it. He turned and bared his teeth at her, hissing. Stopped in her tracks, the teacher demanded Emily remove "the nasty cat".

Something was wrong. Emily told her Apollo had never done anything like this before and that she must go to Grandma Betsy. The whole class, and eventually other classes as well, were all at their classroom windows watching as Apollo ran ahead of Emily and out of the school grounds. They ran all the way home; where they found Grandma Betsy lying on the floor. She had had a small stroke, and though recovering well afterwards, was unable to do all she had done before.

Apollo was her constant companion, and they lived for many years together before old age really caught up with them both. Emily looked after them on leaving school, and after they both died the cottage was sold and she had to find work in the city. To this day Grandma Betsy and Apollo were forever labelled as "the Witch lady and her black cat".

A car is approaching the house; I guess it's the Estate Agent we'd agreed to meet right here. Yes, I am Emily, and I hope to buy the old cottage that was my home. The Agent gives me the keys and we walk through the house.

He doesn't need a sales pitch as I can tell him so much more. Not much has been changed.

We agree the sale without delay. I don't have any doubts whatsoever; I've always wanted to come home.

As he is about to leave, he asks if I could do him a favour; goes to his car and from his briefcase he extracts a book.

"Will you please sign your latest book for me? My wife would love to have your autograph. She loves all your recipes, especially this section." He opens a page that reads, *Grandma B's Beautiful Biscuits – Love comes in many flavours.*

After signing the book, I wave him goodbye. I go inside and straight into Grandma's kitchen and I'm half expecting to see Apollo sitting on the windowsill, waiting for me to start to cook.

THE AUTHOR SAYS...

"Teenage memories of holidays with my aunt in a tiny village in Suffolk, where she was well known for her fantastic cakes. My favourite task was measuring everything on beautiful brass scales."

Fancy That!

Blue facts that make you go "**Wow!**"

◆ **Greeks often wear a blue charm necklace or blue bracelet to ward off the "evil eye".**

◆ In India, paintings of the god Krishna often depict him as having blue skin.

The colour of ocean and sky, blue is perceived as a constant in our lives

Owls are the only birds that can see the colour blue

◆ **Blue ribbon: first place; something as being of the highest quality.**

◆ People are often more productive in blue rooms.

◆ **Mosquitoes are attracted to the colour blue twice as much as to any other colour.**

◆ **Blue is the favoured colour choice for toothbrushes.**

◆ In Mexico, blue is the colour of mourning.

In the United States, post office mailboxes are typically blue

Blueberries are the favourite of blue foods and are renowned for their health benefits

Powder blue is often used in products to promote cleanliness and purity

◆ **Once in a blue moon: an event that occurs infrequently.**

WORDS: BABS BEATON PICTURES: ISTOCKPHOTO, THINKSTOCK

For Auld Lang Syne

Plans for an early night went out of the window when the party started – but that was only the start of the surprises

By Karen Clarke

lare had just settled down with her book when she heard music blaring out from across the road.

She moved to the window and looked out into the frosty night. It was coming from old Mary Fisher's bungalow, its windows lit up like a Christmas tree.

Clare sighed. She'd been planning an early night, but it didn't look like that would be possible now.

Cars were pulling up, and the sound of laughter briefly reminded her of other New Year's Eves she'd spent with Matt. Now he was somewhere else, celebrating with his new wife and baby.

Tears threatened and she went back to her book, but couldn't concentrate now. She turned up the television, but could still feel the throb of the music.

An hour later she'd had enough.

She pulled on her coat and made her way over the road, treading carefully on the icy surface.

She pressed the doorbell and kept her finger there until she heard someone approaching.

"Hello dear, I'm so glad you could come." Mary was wearing a party hat and her bright blue eyes shone a welcome from behind her glasses. "Now quickly, dear. You're letting the cold in."

Clare tried to protest, but was ushered into a pine-scented hallway festooned with fairy-lights, balloons and holly. "Listen, I was wondering if …" she began.

"Let me get you a drink," Mary said, as though she hadn't spoken. "You got my invitation, then?"

"What?" Clare suddenly remembered a plain white envelope among her post, which she hadn't got round to opening.

"Here you are, dear."

Before she knew it, Clare had a glass in her hand and was being escorted into an adjoining room, where a space had been cleared for dancing.

"Do you do this every year?" she shouted over the music, her curiosity

Clare tried to protest, but was ushered into a hallway festooned with balloons

PICTURES: THINKSTOCK ILLUSTRATION: JIM DEWAR

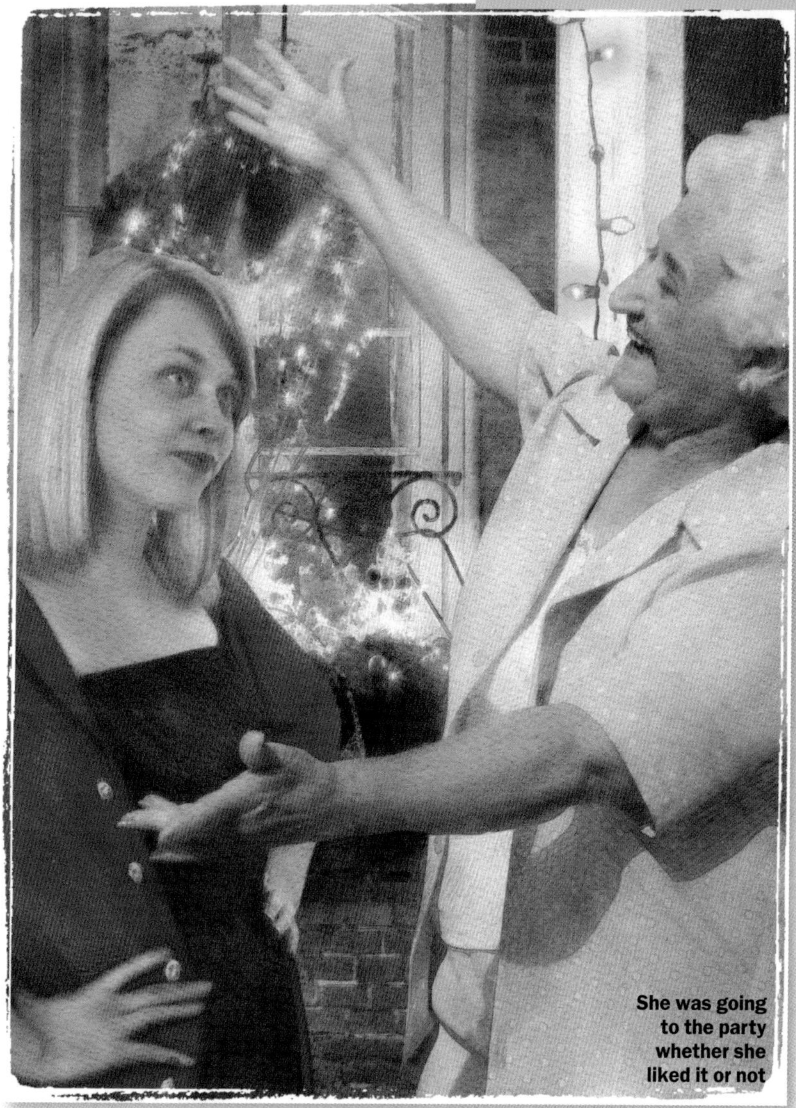

She was going to the party whether she liked it or not

piqued. She and Matt had often gone to parties, but they had never held one at their own home.

"We'll only end up with ruined carpets," Matt used to say, ruffling her hair in his usual annoying way. She didn't miss that, and now she thought about it he'd never liked dancing much either.

"It reminds me I'm alive, having people around." Mary leaned in close and Clare could smell her soft perfume. "My Harry loved a good party. This is my way of keeping his memory alive." Her eyes grew distant, and Clare suddenly wished she'd made more effort to get to know her.

Continued overleaf...

Continued from previous page

She'd seen Mary over the months, going back and forth with her shopping bags, but had never done more than smile, still too raw from her divorce to make new friends.

"It looks fun." Clare's annoyance evaporated as she sipped her wine and tapped her foot to the music.

"We've all got our problems," Mary said unexpectedly. "But it's nice to forget them for a night, and who knows what the New Year will bring?"

She patted Clare's hand then made her way over to where a tall man with wavy dark hair was standing. She said something to him and pointed at Clare, who grew hot under their gaze. She took off her coat, wondering why she didn't just go, but the thought of an early night had lost its appeal.

"Hi, I'm Tom." He appeared in front of her, broad-shouldered, with warm brown eyes. "I see you've met my Gran."

Clare nodded shyly, and smiled as George Michael began an old favourite song she hadn't heard for ages.

It would soon be midnight and they'd probably have to sing and hold hands, but somehow the thought of it wasn't so bad.

"Would you like to dance?" Tom held his hand out.

"Why not?" she said, feeling reckless, and took it.

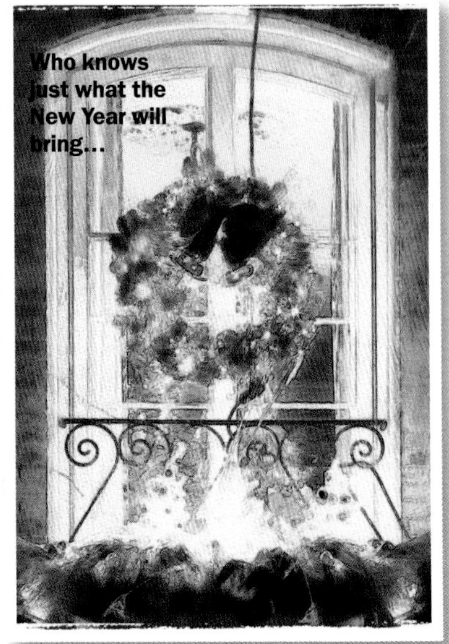

Mary watched from across the room and smiled. She'd had a feeling the music would bring Clare over, and was glad she'd invited her after all.

She looked like a girl who hadn't danced for a while, and it was high time her grandson had some fun, too.

She watched them moving together, tentatively at first, then with more abandon as the night wore on, their faces wreathed in smiles, and after the clock had struck midnight and they'd all sung *Auld Lang Syne*, she lifted her glass in a toast.

"Happy New Year, Harry," she whispered. "I miss you."

It would soon be midnight and they'd probably have to sing and hold hands

THE AUTHOR SAYS...

"The story idea came after observing different approaches to New Year. While some prefer to slip off quietly to bed, others look forward with hope and see it as a time to celebrate."

BRAIN BOOSTERS SOLUTIONS

CODEWORD from page 31

C	E	N	T	R	E	■	R	O	T	A	T	E
■	X	■	R	■	P	■	E	■	W	■	A	■
F	I	X	A	T	I	O	N	■	A	B	L	E
■	S	■	P	■	T	■	A	■	N	■	K	■
S	T	Y	E	■	H	O	L	O	G	R	A	M
■	E	■	Z	■	E	■	■	■	■	■	T	■
I	N	T	E	N	T	■	M	E	M	O	I	R
■	T	■	■	■	■	■	A	■	A	■	V	■
D	I	S	C	O	V	E	R	■	J	E	E	R
■	A	■	L	■	I	■	Q	■	E	■	N	■
A	L	S	O	■	S	Q	U	A	S	H	E	D
■	L	■	U	■	O	■	I	■	T	■	S	■
O	Y	S	T	E	R	■	S	L	Y	E	S	T

KRISS KROSS from page 91

S	T	R	E	T	C	H		M	U	S	T	Y
C		E		A		A	D	O		O		A
A	L	B	U	M	E	N		U	L	C	E	R
R		U		E		K	I	T		K		D
F	I	F	E		A			H	U	E		A
		F	L	U	N	K	E	Y		T	U	G
E			F		T		D		F			E
L	A	B		V	I	C	E	R	O	Y		
E		I	C	E			N		B	E	E	P
G		D		N	O	D		C		O		I
I	N	D	I	E		I	N	H	U	M	A	N
A		E		E	V	E		I		A		N
C	A	R	E	R		T	E	N	A	N	C	Y

MISSING LINK from Page 121

ACROSS: 1 Bomb 3 Masters 7 Jar 8 Times 10 Director 11 Sail 13 Beef 14 Ship 18 Unit 19 Currency 22 Fruit 23 Air 24 Trigger 25 Deer

DOWN: 1 Blonde 2 Major 3 Motion 4 Semi 5 Saddle 6 Bracket 9 Stamp 12 Thermal 13 Brief 15 Bullet 16 Cutter 17 Oyster 20 Nerve 21 Hung

MISSING LINK from page 133

ACROSS: 1 Sling 4 Watch 7 Glue 8 Training 9 Hearts 11 Beef 12 Bulb 14 Door 17 Rush 18 Hammer 19 Personal 21 Word 22 Mince 23 Style

DOWN: 1 Silver 2 Ice 3 Gates 4 Wrapped 5 Tin 6 Hanger 10 Rough 11 Broom 13 Balance 15 Museum 16 Degree 18 Holes 20 Sun 21 Way

SUDOKU From Page 157

3	2	4	6	1	9	7	5	8
9	5	8	7	2	3	6	4	1
6	7	1	8	4	5	9	2	3
7	4	3	5	8	1	2	9	6
2	6	9	4	3	7	1	8	5
8	1	5	9	6	2	3	7	4
4	8	2	1	9	6	5	3	7
5	3	6	2	7	8	4	1	9
1	9	7	3	5	4	8	6	2

1	2	7	8	5	6	4	9	3
6	8	3	4	9	2	1	5	7
4	9	5	1	7	3	2	8	6
8	4	6	9	3	5	7	1	2
7	5	1	6	2	4	8	3	9
9	3	2	7	8	1	5	6	4
5	6	9	2	4	8	3	7	1
2	7	8	3	1	9	6	4	5
3	1	4	5	6	7	9	2	8

WORD WHEEL from page 157

The nine-letter word is JUBILANCE

Wish Upon A Star

For Josh and his dad, there could only be one thing to hope for...

By Barbara Featherstone

She wouldn't come. Not now. All this time, he had kept that small gold nugget of hope shining deep in his heart. The days had whirled by like a flurry of snowflakes and Josh had tried to catch them back, but they spun from his grasp. Then, suddenly, it was Christmas Eve – almost too late for hope, too late for dreams.

It was just like his last birthday party, his tenth birthday. It was mid-January but Dad had surprised him with fireworks. He'd kept back a big box from Bonfire Night, and hidden it in the garage to bring out as a special surprise. After the birthday tea, the balloons, the cake with ten candles, the games and the party bags, Josh's tired and happy guests were collected by their parents and escorted home with goodie bags.

Then it was just Dad and Josh. This was their own special time; the time they spent together every day between tea and Josh's bedtime.

But that night, the night of Josh's tenth birthday, was extra special. He and Dad had waited until first dark, the garden suddenly unfamiliar, the pear tree a silvery ghost shape in the shadows. Josh's cheeks had burned poppy-red from the cold, his breath puffing out like dandelion mist balls.

However he tried, he couldn't catch the glittery sparks of the fireworks

The fireworks had been magic. Josh had been entranced at the crazy spinning of the Catherine wheel; the sparks shooting crimson, emerald, orange and gold, whirling and swirling. He'd roared with delight, flinging off his warm gloves and reaching with bare hands to capture the fiery sparks. But when he'd spread his fingers there was nothing there, nothing at all. Like the snowflakes, the glittery sparks had disappeared.

Then the rockets had gone up. High, high, high – soaring higher still then BANG BANG! And the sparks had shot again, but once more too high and too far, melting like rainbow stars into the velvet darkness.

The sparks from the fireworks that night reminded Josh of his mother, as she got ready for one of her own parties. She'd always looked so beautiful, her green eyes shiny bright, her lustrous dark

Continued overleaf...

PICTURES: THINKSTOCK ILLUSTRATIONS: KIRK HOUSTON

His dad had made his tenth birthday extra special

Continued from previous page

hair coiled high, her face glowing and jewel-bright like the firework sparks. Josh would reach out to touch her pretty dress, a sparkling brooch, or a glittery bracelet. And his mother would laugh as she sat at her dressing table; the light from the diamonds at her ears exploding and dancing, and shattering into starlight.

He hadn't noticed the change at first. He'd been preoccupied with school, homework, swimming lessons, the school football team and his passion for dinosaurs. But suddenly, after one of her parties, his mother hadn't come home.

It was a school day. Josh had been lazing under the duvet, waiting for his mother's familiar call of, "Get a move on, Josh! You'll be late for school, darling!" the delicious smell of coffee, warm milk and toast, and the comforting clatter of breakfast time.

But this time it was Josh's dad who roused him from his bed. And when Josh went downstairs there was a strange stillness in the kitchen. The cereal in his bowl was the wrong one; the milk slopped and was lukewarm; and the only smell that of burnt toast.

His father had turned bright eyes on him, a smile stretched tight across his face. "Your mum's with her friend, Anna, son. She phoned last night. Apparently, the party was going on a bit, so she thought it best if she stayed over. She didn't want to disturb us both by coming in late. I told her fine."

The bright glance had slid away. Josh knew when adults were lying. It was the over-loud cheerfulness, that pasted smile, the eagerness to be off and doing other things.

His dad had driven him to school that morning. Usually Josh took the school bus, but one look at his father's face and he kept silent.

When Josh got home from school that day, his mother was back.

This small disruption to the routine pattern of his life was the first of a smattering that followed. To begin with, the changes were subtle. With the hectic agenda of swimming, football and the dinosaurs, Josh barely noticed them. But over the next few weeks he gradually became more aware, and more disturbed.

His mother's intermittent absences grew more frequent. There were other parties, dances, long shopping excursions, a school reunion, visits to the theatre, a trip to London to attend a West End play. Once his mum went on holiday to Paris for a whole weekend, without Josh and his dad. Bereft of the light and the colour and the bright singing of her, their lives were drab.

Charlie knew everything. She'd answer the questions he couldn't ask his dad

Sometimes Josh would wander into his parents' bedroom, when his dad was at the computer in the study, or in the living room watching TV or a DVD. He would open his mother's wardrobe, softly, and look at the rail of pretty dresses, skirts, jackets, blouses and shoes. Sometimes, he would pad over to the dressing table and peek into his mother's jewellery box, fingering an earring, a brooch, a ring, a bracelet.

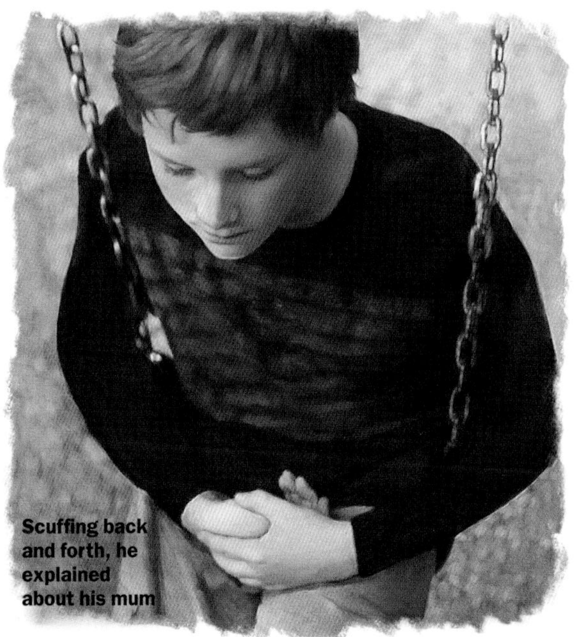
Scuffing back and forth, he explained about his mum

He left everything as he found it. All he was doing was checking it was all still there. As long as her clothes, her jewellery, and her perfume remained, his mother would come home. And one day, she would stay. He had to keep that shining nugget of hope tight snug in his heart.

Josh didn't ask questions. He knew that if he did, he would be diverted with the wrong answers. He also knew that this was his dad's way of protecting him. And, in a topsy-turvy kind of way, not asking questions was Josh's way of protecting his dad.

But Josh needed answers. He needed to understand this strange world of adults. So he asked Charlie.

Charlie went to Josh's school. She was a year younger than him, a small, skinny girl with inquisitive brown eyes and a determinedly pointed chin. But Charlie was cool. Charlie knew everything. Charlie would know the answers. And Charlie was Josh's best friend.

One Saturday, they met up at the local park. They wedged themselves into the baby swings, swinging gently back and forth, scuffing at the rubber surface, while Josh told Charlie all about his mum, and the way she had changed.

After a bit, they transferred to the roundabout. Charlie hung on to the bar as she raced the roundabout round. Josh sat on top, clutching his bit of bar and trying not to feel sick. Then Charlie leapt back on and told Josh the answers to his questions. It took a while, so sometimes the answers were put on hold while Charlie jumped down to revive the flagging roundabout.

Charlie had explained things carefully and calmly, asking questions of her own so she could get the answers right. There was a whole range of possibilities. But from the clues she had wangled from Josh, Charlie thought she'd come up with the right one.

According to Charlie's mum (Charlie eavesdropped a lot – "that's how you learn things, see?") Josh's dad was a lot older than his mum. (Josh hadn't known this.) Josh's dad dyed his hair to make him look younger. (Josh hadn't known this, either.) So, anyway, Josh's dad – most like – had already "sown his wild oats" before he got married to Josh's mum. (Charlie had to explain "wild oats"

Continued overleaf...

Continued from previous page

because Josh got completely the wrong picture.)

Charlie screwed up her nose. Josh's mum was a good mum. She'd stayed at home for absolutely yonks – doing all that boring cooking and housework; putting up with a squalling baby and all those smelly nappies; feeding it day and night; then looking after the baby and its dad for years and years (ten years, put in Josh, eleven next January.)

It was simple, really, concluded Charlie. Josh's mum had missed out on all the fun and decided it was time to sow some wild oats of her own. That's probably what she was doing now – sowing – having parties and holidays and a bit of excitement. And you couldn't really do the sowing with a husband and ten-year-old in tow, could you? Josh's mum was doing something for herself.

There was more question-and-answer in the park shelter while Josh and Charlie perched on the graffiti-spattered bench and munched crisps. Josh learned that there was a great deal more to the world than swimming, football and visits to the dinosaur museum. He suddenly understood the word 'divorce'. Lots of kids at school had divorced parents. Some lived with a single parent; several had parents with a different surname from their own, extended families…

But Josh's parents weren't going to get divorced. Charlie had promised. His mum and his dad loved him to pieces. All Josh had to do, Charlie instructed, was to be patient and wait. After the sowing, his mum would settle down. Everything would be the same as it was before. And Josh wouldn't have to eat the wrong cereal or burnt toast any more.

But time was running out. Doubt began to gnaw away at him.

When it mattered his mother had been there for him these past weeks; for them all. Special times like his dad's birthday party, the time Josh got chicken pox, the school play, a family picnic.

Yet she had missed the last parents' evening at school. Would she miss the most important event of the year, the Christmas Eve carol service in their old village church? Each year Josh and his parents attended as a family, the huge tree scenting the church with a perfume so mysterious it made him want to cry.

And now the time had come, creeping up so softly that Josh was barely aware of its presence. Tonight was Christmas Eve.

Suddenly he knew that if she didn't come back now, she never would again

And suddenly he knew, if she didn't come now, she never would again.

The pain exploded like a million zillion fragments of shattered glass. And yet through the pain there had been that tiny, tiny firefly flicker of hope; that fragile breathless dream.

Christmas Eve. Josh and his father were walking through the hushed village towards the little grey church. They walked slowly and without eagerness, neither speaking, though each knowing the other's thoughts.

As they rounded the lane, they paused. Josh swallowed, clamped shut his eyes, then opened them quick, sifting the shadows, discerning the shape of her. But

there was only the familiarity of neighbours and the calling of soft greetings from the old church doorway.

When his father cried, “Look, son!” Josh spun, arms outstretched ready to enfold her. But his father said, “A falling star, Josh! Quick! Make a wish!”

He watched the star shoot silver across the black sky and he thrust out hands that couldn’t catch it. Then his father touched his arm and they walked on into the church together.

It was chill inside, people’s breath silver-misted. Josh glanced around, trying to concentrate on every detail, trying to suppress any thought of her.

The church was hung with holly; leaves emerald shining, berries glowing scarlet. He breathed in the coldness of the holly, and the sharp, tangy scent of the huge Christmas tree with the silver star on top. Candles had been lit, the flames flickering yellow-gold. He wished it wasn’t so beautiful.

His father rustled the pages of the hymn book they shared. The organist struck up the first carol, “It came upon the midnight clear…”

But Josh forgot to sing. He was looking at the little Nativity scene displayed in front of the church. The Sunday School children set it up every year. Josh stared at the tiny figures of the shepherds, the carved wooden sheep and oxen, and the baby lamb. And behind the crib, the miniature figures of Mary and Joseph – Joseph leaning a little on his staff, but proud and overawed by it all.

The carol had finished now. The choirboys were starting to sing. But Josh didn’t hear them. The soft blue of Mary’s dress and cloak drew his gaze from the grey and brown of the shepherds. Just a soft, soft blue, but so right.

He couldn’t draw his gaze away. So, so right – a baby, a mother and a father. A family. He couldn’t stop staring. He wished that the love and the calmness of the little wooden group could reach out and touch him, do something about the hard, ice-tight feeling in his heart.

Then he heard the snatch of a breath beside him. His father had stopped singing, too. The two of them stood side by side, silently contemplating the little carved figures of the Nativity scene.

It was even colder as they left the church. Josh clutched his coat more tightly about him. Then his father whispered, “Look, Josh!” And Josh raised his head and stretched out his hands to try, perhaps, to catch the falling star once more. Perhaps the same star, perhaps

Continued overleaf...

Continued from previous page

another. But not to make a wish again. Because wishing on a falling star never worked.

Or did it? Because Josh's dad wasn't pointing at a star. He was pointing towards the shadows of a holly bush a little distance from the old church.

He'd imagined this scene a million, zillion times – racing towards her, arms outstretched, enfolding her, loving her. But neither he nor his father moved. Instead it was she who came to them. Even in the faint gold glow from the church, he could tell that she was different. The restlessness had ebbed away. In its place was a quietness and a stillness.

The restlessness had ebbed away. In its place was a quietness, a stillness

She came slowly, gazing up into his father's face and then down into his. The notes from the organ drifted from the church, weaving into the silence.

Her voice when she spoke was hushed.

"I wanted to come into the church with you tonight, but I was afraid. I saw a shooting star and I made a wish. But only you and Josh can make my wish come true." She paused and added gently, "I'd like to come home. But it has to be your decision, yours and Josh's. Because if I come, this time it will be forever."

A soft sigh came from somewhere. Josh's dad looked up at the sky then grinned down at Josh. "We saw a shooting star tonight, didn't we, son?"

Josh nodded. "We made a wish, too, didn't we, Dad?"

The same star, the same wish.

They started back through the village towards home, the three of them linked warmly together. Josh raised his head. Was that another falling star in the sky? But it wasn't a solitary silver star he saw. It was the myriad of fire-glow stars of past winter nights, crazily exploding and dancing and shattering into a million, zillion stars of hope and happiness.

It was Christmas Eve…

THE AUTHOR SAYS…

"At Christmas time, I love the brightly lit streets and houses, the twinkle of Christmas trees in windows. But, sometimes, curtains are closed, the room in darkness. And I wonder."